OUR SINGING WORLD

Singing Together

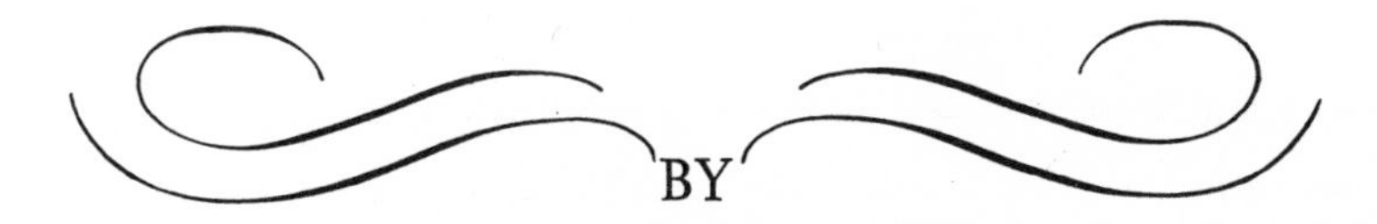

BY

LILLA BELLE PITTS

Professor of Music Education, Teachers College, Columbia University, New York

MABELLE GLENN

Formerly Director of Music, Public Schools, Kansas City, Missouri

LORRAIN E. WATTERS

Director of Music, Public Schools, Des Moines, Iowa

Illustrations by Ruth Wood, Alison Cummings, Alice Freeman, and Marguerite Scott

GINN AND COMPANY

BOSTON · NEW YORK · CHICAGO · ATLANTA · DALLAS · COLUMBUS · PALO ALTO · TORONTO · LONDON

958.4
D

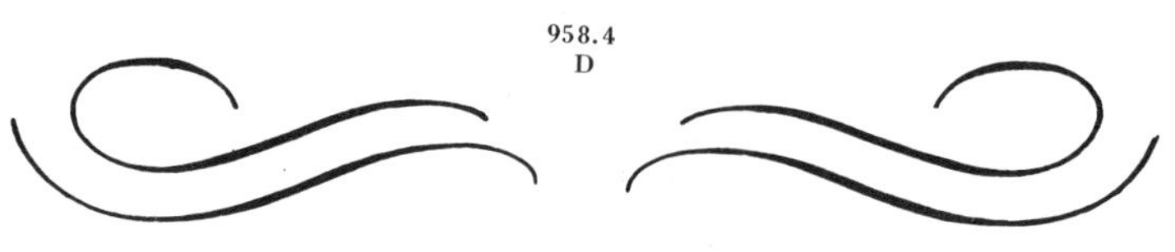

Acknowledgments

Acknowledgment is due to publishers, composers, and authors for permission to reprint songs and poems in this book, as follows:

THE BOY SCOUTS ASSOCIATION, "We're All Together Again," from the *Boy Scout Songbook of England*; CENTRAL CONFERENCE OF AMERICAN RABBIS, "Praise to the Living God," from the *Union Hymnal for Jewish Worship*; CHATTO & WINDUS, "Lone Dog," from *Songs to Save a Soul* by IRENE RUTHERFORD MCLEOD; the composer, "Lullaby on Christmas Eve," by DR. F. MELIUS CHRISTIANSEN; CO-OPERATIVE RECREATION SERVICE, "I Wonder When I Shall Be Married," from the *Handy Play Party Book*; J. CURWEN & SONS LTD., "Fishermen's Evening Song," by permission, from Curwen Edition No. 6268, published by J. CURWEN & SONS LTD., London; DODD, MEAD & COMPANY, "Cradle Song," words by permission of DODD, MEAD & COMPANY, from *The Sceptred Flute* by SAROJINI NAIDU, copyright 1917, 1928 by DODD, MEAD & COMPANY, INC.; the author, "Thanksgiving," by FRANCES FROST; GINN AND COMPANY, "Chinese Evening Song," "Pay with a Smile" and "Shepherds and the Star" from *Rhythms and Rimes*, "Colly, My Cow," "The Fisher Maiden," and "Pietro's Hat" from *Blending Voices*, all copyright 1936, 1943 by GINN AND COMPANY, "My Donkey Diodoro" and "Song of the Cowboy" from *Sing Along*, copyright 1941 by GINN AND COMPANY, "Christmas Lullaby," "Flicka, Will You Dance with Me?" "Give Us the Winter Time," "Halloween Visitor," "The Skaters," "Slumber, Slumber," and "When the Chestnut Leaves Were Falling" from *On Wings of Song*, copyright 1945, 1949 by GINN AND COMPANY; GIRL SCOUTS, "Goin' to Leave Old Texas," from the *Girl Scout Song Book*; The CURTIS PUBLISHING COMPANY and the author, "After School" by MAE WINKLER GOODMAN, from the *Saturday Evening Post*; The H. W. GRAY COMPANY, INC., "La Paloma Blanca" ("Come, My Dove"), from *Folk Songs from Mexico and South America*; MISS ELEANOR HAGUE and the AMERICAN FOLKLORE SOCIETY, "There Grew a Rosy Maid" and "A Golden Cage Was Hanging," from *Spanish American Folk Songs*; HARCOURT, BRACE AND COMPANY, "Wings and Wheels" ("Such Joy") from *Magpie Lane* by NANCY BYRD TURNER, copyright 1927 by HARCOURT, BRACE AND COMPANY, INC.; HARVARD UNIVERSITY PRESS, "Mister Rabbit," reprinted by permission of the publishers from DOROTHY SCARBOROUGH'S *On the Trail of Negro Folk-Songs*, Cambridge, Mass.: HARVARD UNIVERSITY PRESS, 1925; WILLIAM HEINEMANN, LTD., London, "Cradle Song" by SAROJINI NAIDU; HENRY HOLT AND COMPANY, "Tired Tim" and "I Saw Three Witches" from *Collected Poems, 1901–1918*, by WALTER DE LA MARE, copyright, 1920, by HENRY HOLT AND COMPANY, INC., copyright, 1948, by WALTER DE LA MARE; ALFRED A. KNOPF, "Bells in the Country," reprinted from *The Green Leaf* by ROBERT NATHAN, copyright 1922, 1950, by ROBERT NATHAN, by permission of ALFRED A. KNOPF, INC., and "The Blacktail Range" ("I'm a Roving Cowboy") and "The Cowboy's Lament" ("My Home's in Montana"), reprinted from *Singing Cowboy* by MARGARET LARKIN, by permission of ALFRED A. KNOPF, INC., copyright 1931 by ALFRED A. KNOPF, INC.; ESTATE OF JOHN A. LOMAX, "The Cowboy's Life" from *Cowboy Songs and Other Frontier Ballads*, by JOHN A. LOMAX; THE MACMILLAN COMPANY, "Night" (excerpt) from *Stars Tonight*, copyright 1930 by SARA TEASDALE FILSINGER and used with permission of THE MACMILLAN COMPANY, "Washed in Silver" (excerpt), from *Songs of Clay* by JAMES STEPHENS, copyright 1915, 1943, by THE MACMILLAN COMPANY and used with their permission, "Abraham Lincoln Walks at Midnight" (excerpt), from *The Congo and Other Poems* by VACHEL LINDSAY, copyright 1914, 1942 by THE MACMILLAN COMPANY and used with their permission; DR. MARÍA CADILLA DE MARTÍNEZ, "Palomita Blanca" ("White Dove"), from *Cantos y Juegos Infantiles de Puerto Rico* by DR. MARTÍNEZ; MAYFAIR MUSIC CORP., "'Leven-Cent Cotton (Forty-Cent Meat)," used by permission of the copyright owner, MAYFAIR MUSIC CORP.; the author, "Skating Song," by CHRISTOPHER MORLEY; OXFORD UNIVERSITY PRESS, "The Lily Princess," from *A Year of Japanese Epigrams* by WILLIAM N. PORTER; ARTHUR S. PEDERSON, "A Summer Morning" by RACHEL FIELD; REVEREND VINCENT PISEK, "The Quest" ("Good Night") from *Twenty-two Bohemian Folk Songs*; THEODORE PRESSER COMPANY, "Sunrise Call" and "Sunset Song" from *Traditional Songs of the Zuñi Indians*, edited by CARLOS TROYER, and "Slumber" by AUBER FORESTIER, from *Songs from the North*, published and copyrighted by the OLIVER DITSON COMPANY and reproduced by permission; FLEMING H. REVELL COMPANY, "Hear Our Prayer, O Lord," by GEORGE WHELPTON, from *New Hymnal for American Youth*; RALPH FLETCHER SEYMOUR, "Peña" (*In the Plaza*) and "Tres Años Hace" (*Mariquita*) from *Spanish Folk Songs from New Mexico*, by MARY VAN STONE; SMITHSONIAN INSTITUTION, "Daylight," from Part 2 of the *Twenty-second Annual Report of the Bureau of American Ethnology*; TEXAS FOLK-LORE SOCIETY, "Don't Let Your Watch Run Down"; GORDON V. THOMPSON, Toronto, "O Canada"; JANET TOBITT and M. SINCLAIR, "Kookaburra" from *Yours for a Song*; WHITMAN PUBLISHING COMPANY, "Our Flag" from *365 Bedtime Nursery Rimes*; THE WOMAN'S PRESS, "Swiftly Flowing Labe" ("Czech Walking Song") by FJERIL HESS, from *YWCA Song Book*, copyright 1925, by permission of THE WOMAN'S PRESS, 600 Lexington Avenue, New York 22, New York. The melody of "Deep in the Forest" is from *American Primitive Music* by FREDERICK BURTON, published by MOFFAT, YARD AND COMPANY, 1909.

In the case of some poems for which acknowledgment is not given, we have earnestly endeavored to find the original source and to procure permission for their use, but without success.

Contents

SONGS WE KNOW · (Page 7)

[Titles in italics indicate instrumental selections.]

Oh! Susanna, 7
Frog Went a-Courtin', 8
My Home's in Montana, 9
'Liza Jane, 10 (Orchestration, 10–11)
Come, Thou Almighty King, 12
Home, Sweet Home, 12
Rig-a-Jig-Jig, 13
Golden Slumbers Kiss Your Eyes, 14

ABOUT FOLKS · (Page 15)

SING, SING TOGETHER

We're All Together Again, 16
Smiles, Just like the Sunshine, 16
Sing Together, 17
Now Come On, 18
Swinging, 18
Such Joy, 19
Czech Walking Song, 19
Swiss Walking Song, 20
Stodola Pumpa, 21
Wait for the Wagon, 22

JUST FOR FUN

The Animal Fair, 23
Ain't Gonna Rain, 24
Peter Piper, 24
One More River, 25
Arithmetic Song, 26
Young Woman with a Cane, 27
Tired Tim, 28
The Man in the Moon, 28

SINGING GAMES

All around the Shu-Round, 29
Coffee Grows on White Oak Trees, 30
Put Your Little Foot, 31
Shoo Fly, 32
Swing on the Corner, 33
Sweetheart out a-Hunting, 34
Captain Jinks, 35
Three Dukes, 36

DIALOGUE AND DANCE SONGS

The Bold Soldier, 38
The Brave Knight, 39
Flicka, Will You Dance with Me? 40
Come, My Dove, 41
The Fisher Maiden, 42 (Orchestration, 42–43)
There Grew a Rosy Maid, 44
Pay with a Smile, 44
Mariquita, 45
In the Plaza, 46 (Orchestration, 47–48)
As I Went Walking down the Street, 49
Sourwood Mountain, 50
I Wonder When I Shall Be Married, 50
At the Spinning Wheel, 51

SINGING AT WORK

Drill, Ye Tarriers, 52
Work on the Railroad, 53
The Ballit of the Boll Weevil, 54
'Leven-Cent Cotton and Forty-Cent Meat, 55
I'm a Roving Cowboy, 56
The Railroad Corral, 57
Goin' to Leave Ol' Texas, 58
A Song of the Cowboy, 59
The Cowboy's Life, 60
Round the Campfire, 60
Eating Goober Peas, 61
The Erie Canal, 62
Don't Let Your Watch Run Down, 63
A Hundred Years Ago, 64
Cape Cod Chantey, 64
Fishermen's Evening Song, 65
Nile Boatman's Song, 66
The Blacksmith, 66
The Blacksmith Sings Merrily, 67
Buy My Flowers, 68
Past Three o'Clock, 69
De Bezem, 69

HOME AND FAMILY

Old Folks at Home, 70
Memories, 71
Peacefully, My Baby, Sleep, 72
Old Gaelic Lullaby, 73
Hush-a-by, Baby, 73
Slumber, 74
Sleep, My Bonny, Blue-eyed Little Treasure, 76
Winkum, Winkum, 76
Lullaby and Good Night, 77
Cradle Song, 78
Sleep, Sleep, My Darling, 79
Slumber, Slumber, 80
Good Night to You All, 80
Good Night, 81

SONGS OF WORSHIP

How Brightly Shines the Morning Star, 82
Jacob's Ladder, 83
When Moses Smote the Water, 83
Goin' to Ride up in the Chariot, 84
There's a Little Wheel a-Turnin' in My Heart, 85
Holy Spirit, Gift Divine, 85
Faith of Our Fathers, 86 (Orchestration, 86–87)
Praise to the Lord, 88
But the Lord Is Mindful of His Own, 88
Our Heavenly Father, Source of Love, 89
Hear Our Prayer, O Lord, 89
Praise to the Living God, 90
Blessed Are the Pure in Heart, 90

SONGLAND PEOPLE

Sweet Betsy from Pike, 91
Cindy, 92
Mistress Shady, 93
Pietro's Hat, 94
A Trip to Town, 94
Billy Boy, 95

MUSIC MAKERS

Johann Sebastian Bach: Brief Biography, 96
My Heart Ever Faithful, 97
Jesu, Joy of Man's Desiring, 98 (Orchestration, 99)
Minuet in G Major, 100
Minuet in G Minor, 101
George Frederick Handel: Brief Biography, 102–103
He Shall Feed His Flock, 104
Largo from "Xerxes," 105
Melody from the Opera "Rinaldo," 106

Happy Holidays

HALLOWEEN

Halloween Visitor, 107

THANKSGIVING

Now Thank We All Our God, 108
Prayer of Thanksgiving, 109
Come, Ye Thankful People, Come, 110 (Orchestration, 110–111)

CHRISTMAS

Christmas Bells, 112
Pray God Bless, 112
Silent Night, 113
O Little Town of Bethlehem, 114
Shepherds and the Star, 114
Christmas Lullaby, 115
Carol of the Grasses, 116
O Mary, 116
Lullaby on Christmas Eve, 117
Hark! the Herald Angels Sing, 118 (Orchestration, 118–119)
The Wondrous Child, 120
The Angels in Our Fields, 121
On a Winter Morning, 122
The Twelve Days of Christmas, 123

PATRIOTIC DAYS

The Star-Spangled Banner, 124
America, 126 (Orchestration, 127)
Dixie, 128
The Marines' Hymn, 129
O Canada! 130

EASTER

A New Created World, 131 (Orchestration, 131–134)

THE WONDERFUL WORLD OUTSIDE · (Page 135)

MORNING AND EVENING

A Summer Morning, 136
Morning Is Come, 137
The Morning Is Bright, 137
The Sunrise Call, 138
Sunset Song, 139
Deep in the Forest, 140
Evensong, 140
Chinese Evening Song, 141
The Planets, 142
Little Star, 142
Moon and Her Children, 143
Song on a Hilltop, 144

WIND AND WATER

Song of the Breezes, 145
Who Has Seen the Wind? 146
Good-by, 146
A Boat, a Boat to Cross the Ferry, 147
Come, Ye Maidens, 147
Lightly Row, 148
Music of the River, 149

The Seasons

AUTUMN

Harvest Fun, 150
When the Chestnut Leaves Were Falling, 151 (Orchestration, 151)
Autumn Is a Painter, 152
Indian Summer, 153

WINTER

The Skaters, 154
Signs of Winter, 155
Give Us the Wintertime, 156
The Sleighride, 157

SPRING

I Heard It in the Valley, 158
Spring Has Come, 159
Spring Song, 160
Trout Brook in Spring, 161
Song of the Cuckoo, 161
May Day Carol, 162
The Lily Princess, 162
Bluebonnets, 163

CREATURES GREAT AND SMALL

White Dove, 164
Kookaburra, 164
A Golden Cage Was Hanging, 165
Nightingale in the Wood, 165
Lorita, 166
Lone Dog, 166
Sepp Has a Little Hen, 167
Tuku, Tuku, Tuu I'm Calling, 168
White Llamas, 169
Colly, My Cow, 169
Fola, Fola Blakken, 170
Mister Rabbit, 172
The Fox and the Hare, 173
Sweetly Sings the Donkey, 174
The Last Will and Testament of the Gray Mule, 174
On the Road to Willamolay, 175
My Donkey Diodoro, 176

ABOUT SINGING THINGS · (Page 177)

BELLS

The Bell, 178
Bells above the Chapel, 179

MUSIC AND MACHINES

The Wabash Cannonball, 180
A Bicycle Built for Two, 181

WE SING AND PLAY

Listen When the Orchestra Begins, 182
Ring, Ring the Banjo! 183
Peter, the Fiddler, 184
The Fiddlers' Tune, 185
Skip to My Lou, 186 (Orchestration, 187)
The Street Band, 188
The Marching Band, 189
The Tootin' Turk, 190 (Orchestration, 191)
The Royal Trumpeter, 192

SHINING HOURS · (page 193)

Hansel and Gretel, 194

ALPHABETICAL INDEX OF SONGS · (page 214)

Here's an adventure! what awaits
Beyond these closed, mysterious gates?
Whom shall I meet, where shall I go?
Beyond the lovely land I know?
Above the sky, across the sea?
What shall I learn and feel and be?
Open, strange doors, to good or ill!
I hold my breath a moment still
Before the magic of your look.
What shall you do to me, O Book?
Anonymous

Oh! Susanna
Oh! Susanna
Oh! Susanna

SONGS WE KNOW

Oh! Susanna
Stephen Collins Foster
Lively
1. I · came from Al - a - bam - a, With my ban - jo on my knee, I'm ·
2. I · had a dream the oth - er night When ev-'ry-thing was still; I ·
goin' to Lou' - si - a - na, There my true love for to see; It ·
thought I saw Su - san - na dear, A - com - ing down the hill; A ·
rained all night the day I left, The weath-er it was dry, The ·
buck-wheat cake was in her mouth, A tear was in her eye; Says ·
sun so hot I froze to death, Su - san - na, don't you cry.
I, "I'm com - ing from the South, Su - san - na, don't you cry."
Chorus
Oh! Su - san - na, Oh, don't you cry for me, I've ·
come from Al - a - bam - a With my ban - jo on my knee.

Frog Went A-Courtin'

Mississippi Version

With humor
F
dm
C7
F
F

1. A frog went a-court-in', he did ride, uh, huh! A frog went a-court-in',
2. He rode up · to Miss Mous-ie's door, uh, huh! He rode up · to Miss

B♭
F
C7
F

he did ride · Sword and pis - tol by his side, uh, huh!
Mous- ie's door, A place he'd nev - er been be - fore, uh, huh!

3. Miss Mousie she came tripping down, uh, huh!
   In a brand new hat and her Sunday gown, uh, huh!

4. Mister Frog took Mousie on his knee, uh, huh!
   And said, "Miss Mousie, won't you marry me, uh, huh?"

5. "Oh, not without Uncle Rat's consent, uh, huh!
   Could I think of marrying the President, uh, huh!"

6. Uncle Rat right then came riding home, uh, huh!
   Said, "Who's come here while I was gone, uh, huh?"

7. "A nice young man of eighty-three, uh, huh!
   Who says he wants to marry me, uh, huh!"

8. Old Rat he laughed and shook his fat sides, uh, huh!
   To think his niece would be a bride, uh, huh!

9. Oh, where will the wedding supper be, uh, huh?
   'Way down yonder in a hollow tree, uh, huh!

10. The first to come was a big white moth, uh, huh!
    And around her neck was a table cloth, uh, huh!

11. The next to come was an old red hen, uh, huh!
    Tuning up her fiddle to please the men, uh, huh!

12. Oh, next to come was a black old flea, uh, huh!
Strumming a banjo on his knee, uh, huh!

13. Next to come was brown muley cow, uh, huh!
She tried to dance but didn't know how, uh, huh!

14. The next to come was a betsy bug uh, huh!
Who brought lemonade in a little brown jug, uh, huh!

15. And then there came our old gray cat, uh, huh!
Who said, "I'll put an end to that, uh, huh."

16. Miss Mousie scampered up the wall, uh, huh!
Her right foot slipped and she got a bad fall, uh, huh!

17. Mister Frog swam out into the lake, uh, huh!
And got swallowed up by a long green snake, uh, huh!

18. Miss Mousie sat and cried and cried, uh, huh!
Because her husband had gone and died, uh, huh!

My Home's in Montana

Paraphrase from "Singing Cowboy" — Cowboy Song

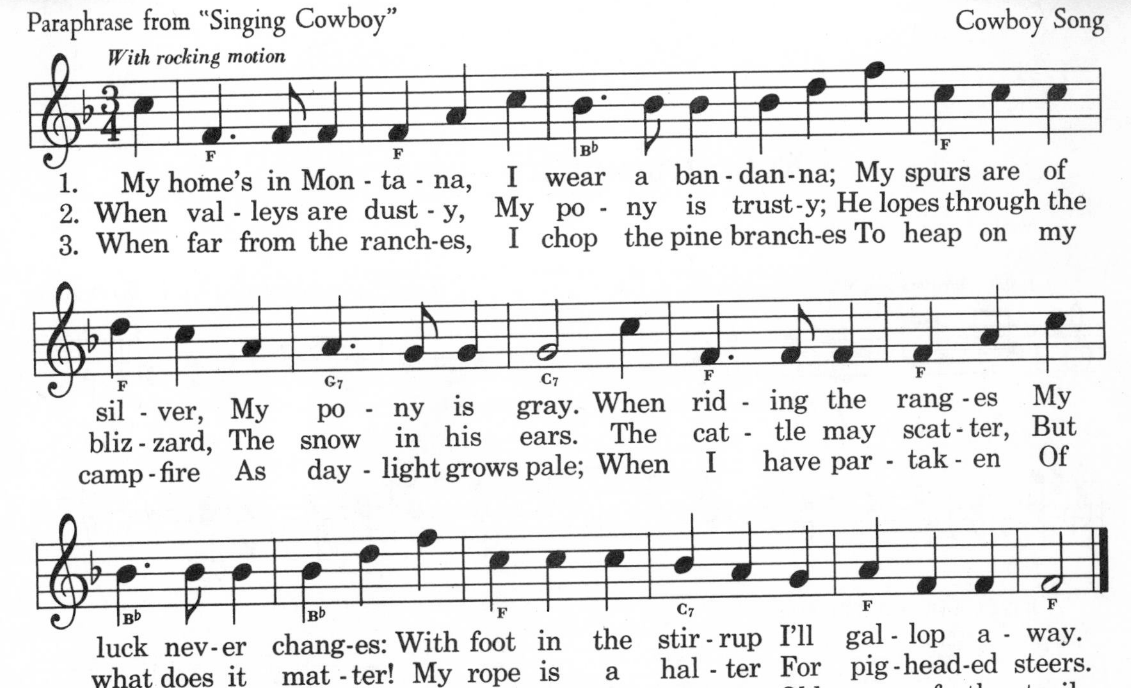
With rocking motion
1. My home's in Mon - ta - na, I wear a ban - dan - na; My spurs are of
2. When val - leys are dust - y, My po - ny is trust - y; He lopes through the
3. When far from the ranch - es, I chop the pine branch - es To heap on my
sil - ver, My po - ny is gray. When rid - ing the rang - es My
bliz - zard, The snow in his ears. The cat - tle may scat - ter, But
camp - fire As day - light grows pale; When I have par - tak - en Of
luck nev - er chang - es: With foot in the stir - rup I'll gal - lop a - way.
what does it mat - ter! My rope is a hal - ter For pig - head - ed steers.
beans and of ba - con, I whis - tle a mer - ry Old song of the trail.

'Liza Jane

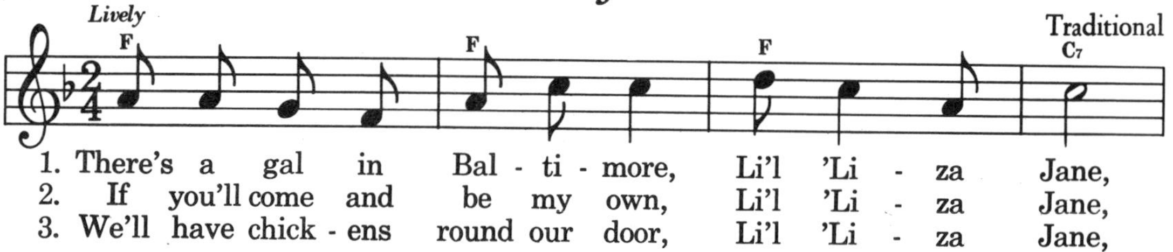
Lively
Traditional
F F F C7
1. There's a gal in Bal - ti - more, Li'l 'Li - za Jane,
2. If you'll come and be my own, Li'l 'Li - za Jane,
3. We'll have chick - ens round our door, Li'l 'Li - za Jane,

F F C7 F
She's the one that I a - dore, Li'l 'Li- - za Jane.
We'll eat ham and sweet corn pone, Li'l 'Li - za Jane.
Brus - sels car - pet on our floor, Li'l 'Li - za Jane.

Chorus
F B♭ F F F B♭ F C7 F
O E - li - za, li'l 'Li - za Jane, O E - li - za, li'l 'Li - za Jane.

Orchestration for 'Liza Jane

Violins and flutes play the voice parts.

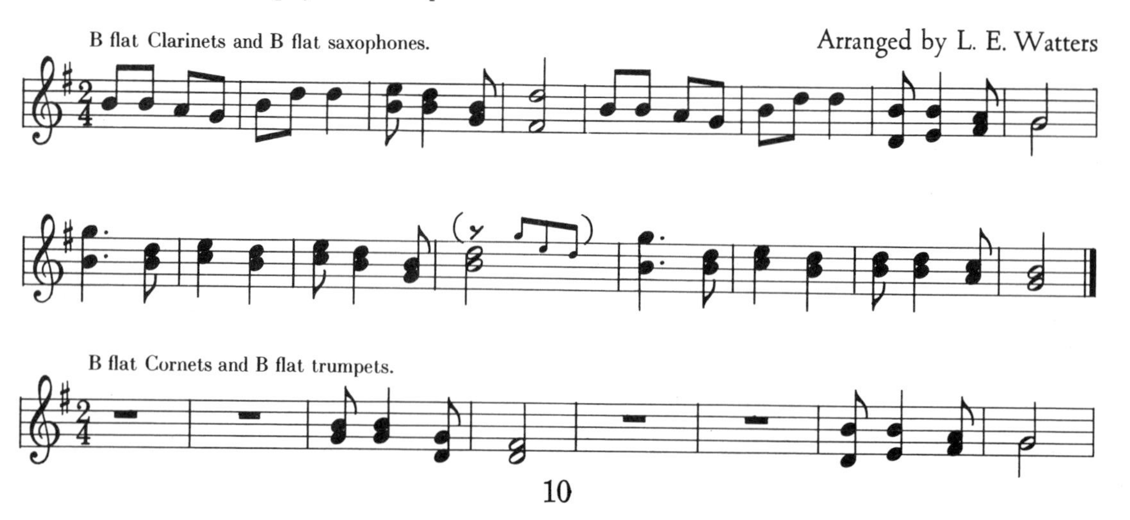
B flat Clarinets and B flat saxophones.
Arranged by L. E. Watters
B flat Cornets and B flat trumpets.

(Cornets and trumpets continued)
E flat Altos (mellophones) and E flat saxophones.
Cellos, trombones and baritones.
Drums.

Come, Thou Almighty King

George Whitfield's Hymn Book, 1757

Felice de Giardini

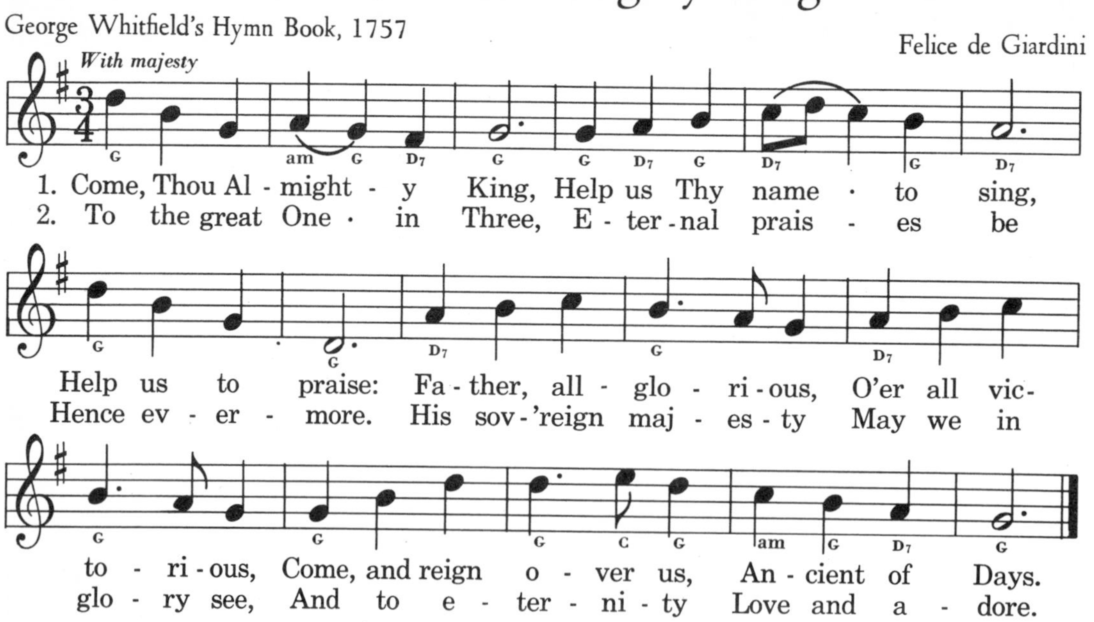
With majesty
G am G D7 G G D7 G D7 G D7
1. Come, Thou Al - might - y King, Help us Thy name · to sing,
2. To the great One · in Three, E - ter - nal prais - es be
G G D7 G D7
Help us to praise: Fa - ther, all - glo - ri - ous, O'er all vic-
Hence ev - er - more. His sov - 'reign maj - es - ty May we in
G G G C G am G D7 G
to - ri - ous, Come, and reign o - ver us, An - cient of Days.
glo - ry see, And to e - ter - ni - ty Love and a - dore.

Home, Sweet Home

John Howard Payne

Henry Rowley Bishop

1. 'Mid · pleas - ures and pal - a - ces though we may roam, Be it
2. How · sweet 'tis to sit 'neath a fond fa - ther's smile, And the
ev - er so hum - ble, there's no · place like home. A
cares of a moth - er to soothe · and be - guile; Let
charm from the skies seems to hal - low us there, Which,
oth - ers de - light 'mid new pleas - ures to roam, But

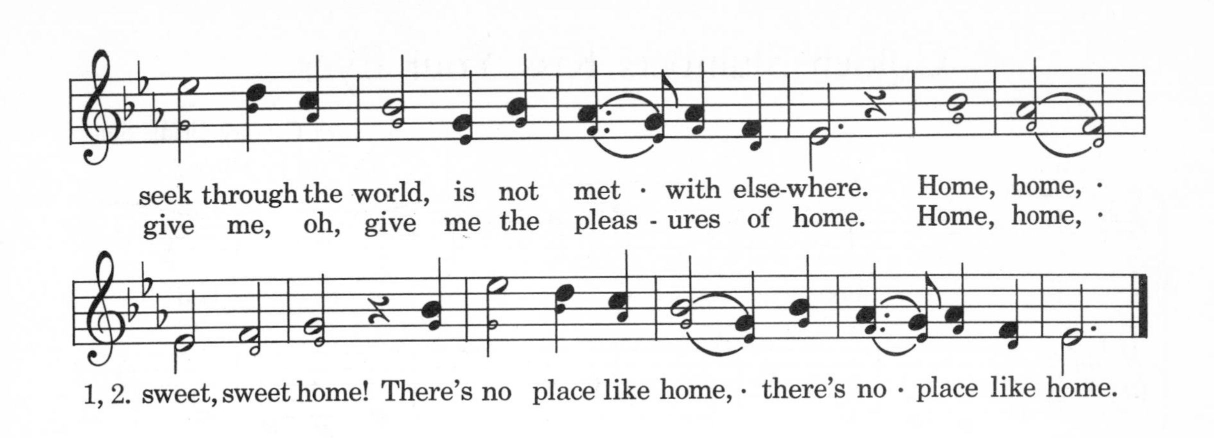
seek through the world, is not met · with else-where. Home, home, ·
give me, oh, give me the pleas - ures of home. Home, home, ·
1, 2. sweet, sweet home! There's no place like home, · there's no · place like home.

Rig-a-Jig-Jig

Briskly
Singing Game
As I was walk-ing down the street, Heigh-o, heigh-o, heigh - o, heigh-o,
A pret - ty girl I chanced to meet, Heigh - o, heigh-o, heigh - o.
(nice young man)
Rig - a - jig -jig, and a - way we go, A - way we go, a - way we go;
Rig - a - jig - jig, and a - way we go, Heigh - o, heigh-o, heigh - o.

Golden Slumbers Kiss Your Eyes

17th Century Cradle Song
Descant by Mildred Guthrie

Smoothly
Loo . . . . Loo .
Gold - en slum - bers kiss your eyes, Smiles · a - wait you
. . . . . Loo . . . .
when you rise; Sleep, pret-ty loved · one, Do · not cry · and
Sleep! Sleep! Lull - a - by, lull - a - by.
I will sing a lull - a - by, Lull - a - by,
Lull - a - by, lull - a, lull - a - by. .
lull - a - by, lull - a - by. .

ABOUT FOLKS

There is no music anywhere
Like children's voices in the air.

Like crystal bells they peal and ring
They never really speak . . . they SING.

But, oh, their cries when school is out—
A song . . . a cheer . . . a bell . . . a SHOUT!

Mae Winkler Goodman

Sing, Sing Together

We're All Together Again

In march time
so (5) do (1)
Greeting Song
G G C E7 am
We're all to - geth - er a - gain, We're here, we're here!
A7 A7 D7 D7
We're all to - geth - er a - gain, We're here, we're here!
fa (4) la (6)
G G7 C C
Who knows when we'll be all to - geth - er a - gain,
ti (7) so (5)
D7 D7 G G
Sing - ing all to - geth - er a - gain, We're here, we're here!

Smiles, Just Like the Sunshine

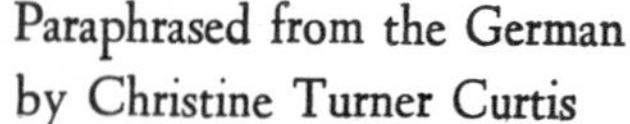
Paraphrased from the German
by Christine Turner Curtis

Happily
3 (mi)
Hans George Nägeli
Friends, let us be joy - ful, Light-heart-ed in work and in play.
1, 2
Fine
Smiles, just like the sun-shine, Turn night in-to day. day.

1. Though skies should dark-en and thun-der roar, Though storms should break o-ver
2. Though roads be nar-row and steep the hill, We'll make the jour-ney in

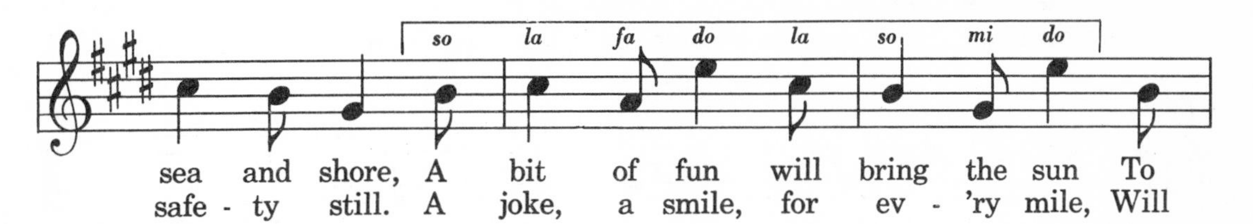
so la fa do la so mi do
sea and shore, A bit of fun will bring the sun To
safe - ty still. A joke, a smile, for ev - 'ry mile, Will

D.C. al Fine
light - en the sky as be - fore.
short - en the way with good will.
Sing Together
Round
1. do (1)
G G G D7 G
Sing, sing to - geth - er, mer - ri - ly, mer - ri - ly sing;
2.
G G G D7 G
Sing, sing to - geth - er, mer - ri - ly, mer - ri - ly, sing;
3.
G G G D7 G
Sing, sing, sing, sing.

Now Come On
Old Round
1. do (1)
2.
3.
Now come on, you can - not catch us, For we have the start, you know.
Hear them say what we are say - ing As we on to - geth - er go.
Swinging
Jane Rensen
la mi ri mi do la
Down and up we're swing - ing, Down and up we're swing - ing.
la si la
Down and up we're swing - ing, To and fro.
la la si la fa re
Down and up we're swing - ing, Up a - bove the tree tops;

Down and up, and down and up, And down and up we go.

Such Joy

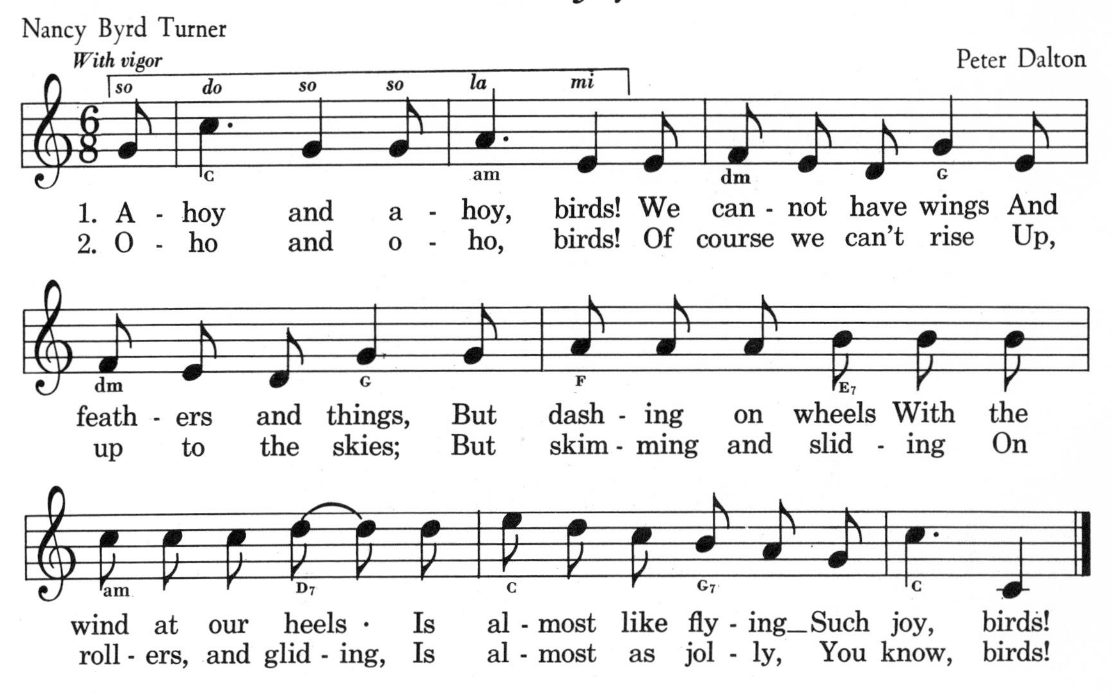
Nancy Byrd Turner
Peter Dalton
With vigor
so do so so la mi
C am dm G dm G F E7 am D7 C G7 C
1. A - hoy and a - hoy, birds! We can - not have wings And
2. O - ho and o - ho, birds! Of course we can't rise Up,
feath - ers and things, But dash - ing on wheels With the
up to the skies; But skim - ming and slid - ing On
wind at our heels · Is al - most like fly - ing_Such joy, birds!
roll - ers, and glid - ing, Is al - most as jol - ly, You know, birds!

Czech Walking Song

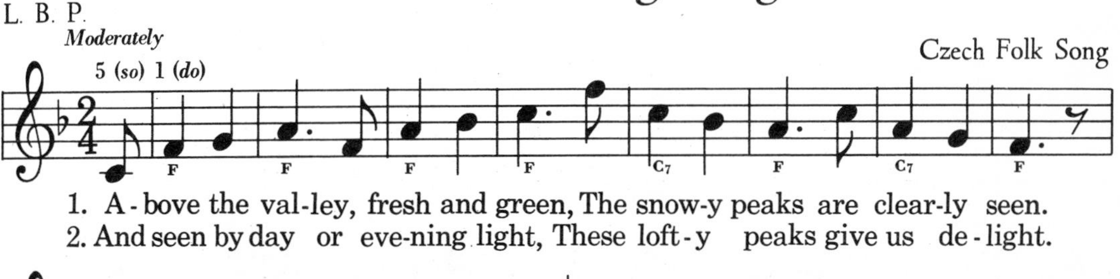
L. B. P.
Moderately
Czech Folk Song
5 (so) 1 (do)
F F F F C7 F C7 F
1. A-bove the val-ley, fresh and green, The snow-y peaks are clear-ly seen.
2. And seen by day or eve-ning light, These loft-y peaks give us de-light.

F F F C7 F
1,2. Rush-ing, rush - ing down be - low, Swift - ly flows the riv - er,

F F F C7 F
Rush-ing, rush - ing down be - low, Swift-ly flows the riv - er.

I know not where the white road runs, nor what the blue hills are,
But a man can have the sun for friend, and for his guide a star.

Gerald Gould

Swiss Walking Song

Translated by Margareta Wassali

Johann Lüthi

Gaily

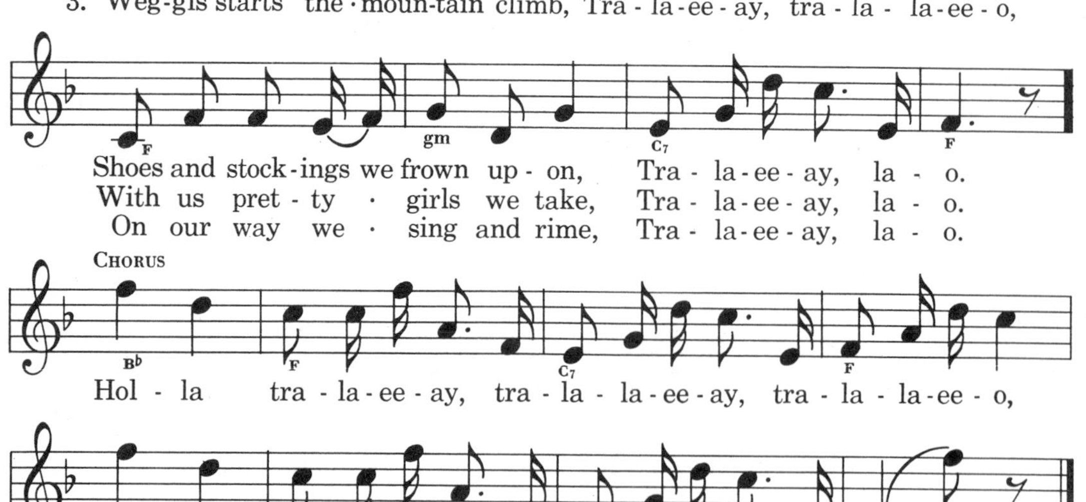
so (5) do (1)
1. From Lu-cerne to · Weg-gis town, Tra-la-ee-ay, tra-la-la-ee-o,
2. When we row a-cross the lake, Tra-la-ee-ay, tra-la-la-ee-o,
3. Weg-gis starts the·moun-tain climb, Tra-la-ee-ay, tra-la-la-ee-o,
Shoes and stock-ings we frown up-on, Tra-la-ee-ay, la-o.
With us pret-ty · girls we take, Tra-la-ee-ay, la-o.
On our way we · sing and rime, Tra-la-ee-ay, la-o.
CHORUS
Hol-la tra-la-ee-ay, tra-la-la-ee-ay, tra-la-la-ee-o,
Hol-la tra-la-ee-ay, tra-la-la-ee-ay, la-o.

4. When we reach the mountain top,
There we dance and skip and hop.

5. Out across the vale we sing,
All the countryside will ring.

Stodola Pumpa

H. L. P.

Czech Walking Song

Leisurely
so (5)

1. Stroll-ing a - long as night-fall ends the day, Sweet-scent-ed breez - es
2. Walk-ing a - long, we're sing-ing as we go; Un - der the stars the

whis - per on their way. Un - der the stars we slow - ly stroll a - long
night winds soft - ly blow. Up in the hills we hear a night-in - gale

While dis - tant hills re - ech - o with our song. *Hey!*
Sing - ing his song out o - ver hill and dale. *Hey!*

CHORUS
much faster
Sto - do - la, sto - do - la, sto - do - la pum - pa,

Sto-do - la pum - pa, sto - do - la pum - pa, Sto-do - la, sto - do - la,

sto - do - la pum - pa, Sto - do - la pum - pa, pum, pum, pum.

"*Stodola pumpa*" are Czech words for "barn pump."

Wait for the Wagon
R. B. Buckley
Brightly
R. B. Buckley
5 (so)
1. Will you come with me, my Phyl-lis, To yon blue moun-tain free? Where blos-soms smell the sweet-est, Come, rove a-long with me. It's ev-'ry Sun-day morn-ing, When I am by your side, We'll jump in-to the wag-on, And all take a ride.
2. Where the riv-er runs like sil-ver, And birds they sing so sweet, I have a cab-in, Phyl-lis, And some-thing good to eat. Come, lis-ten to my sto-ry, It will re-lieve my heart, So jump in-to the wag-on, And off we will start!
do (1). . . . . . . do . . . . so (5) . . . . do . . . . .
do. . . . . do. . . . . . . fa (4) . . . so . . . . do. . . . .
do. . . . . do. . . . . . . so . . . . do. . . . .
do. . . . . do. . . . . fa . . so . . . . do
Chorus
Wait for the wag-on, Wait for the wag-on,
do. . . . . do. . . . . . do. . . . . fa . . . . . .
Wait for the wag-on and we'll all take a ride.
do. . . . . do. . . . . fa . . . so . . . . . . do
C G7 F

Some of you will enjoy singing a "chording" part to this song. The singing names (or numbers) tell what tones to sing for this part.

Just for Fun

I would, if I could,
If I couldn't, how could I?
I couldn't, unless I could, could I?

Folk Saying

The Animal Fair

With humor

Traditional

mi (3)
C C C C
I went to the an - i - mal fair, · The birds and the beasts were there. ·

G7 G7 G7 C
The old ra-coon by the light of the moon Was comb-ing her au-burn hair. ·

C C C C
The fun - ni - est was the monk, · He climbed up the el - e-phant's trunk, ·

G7 G7 G7 C
The el-e-phant sneezed and fell on his knees, And what be-came of the monk? ·

When all of you have sung this song through once, a group of you may sing, "The monk, the monk," repeating it while the rest of you sing the song over again.

The monk, the monk, the monk, the monk.

Ain't Gonna Rain

Plantation Song

Lively
G G G G G G D7 D7 D7 D7 D7 D7 D7 D7 G G
(so) (do)
1. It ain't gon - na rain, it ain't gon - na rain, It ain't gon - na rain no more. (no more) Come on · ev - 'ry - bod - y · now, Ain't gon - na rain no more. (no more)
2. Oh, what did the black - bird say to the crow? It ain't gon - na rain no more. (no more) Ain't gon - na hail and ain't gon - na snow, Ain't gon - na rain no more. (no more)
3. Now bake them · bis - cuits good and · brown. It ain't gon - na rain no more. (no more) Swing your · la - dies round and · round. Ain't gon - na rain no more. (no more)

Peter Piper

Traditional

Caroline Hammond

As fast as you can
do (1)
G D7 G D7 G am D7 G
Pe - ter Pi - per picked a peck of pick - led pep - pers,
A peck of pick - led pep - pers Pe - ter Pi - per picked.

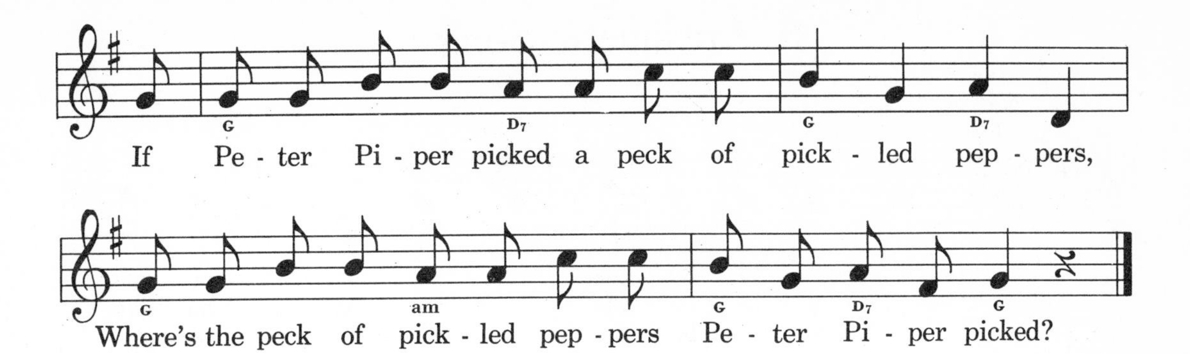
G
D7
G
D7
If Pe - ter Pi - per picked a peck of pick - led pep - pers,
G
am
G
D7
G
Where's the peck of pick - led pep - pers Pe - ter Pi - per picked?

One More River

American Negro

Not too fast
1. Old No - ah built him - self an ark. One more riv - er to cross.
2. The an - i - mals came two by two. One more riv - er to cross.
3. The an - i - mals came three by three. One more riv - er to cross.
He built it out of hick -'ry bark. One more riv - er to cross.
The el - e - phant and kan - ga - roo. One more riv - er to cross.
The ba - boon and the chim - pan - zee. One more riv - er to cross.
Chorus
One more riv - er, And that wide riv - er is Jor - dan,
One more riv - er, There's one more riv - er to cross.

4. The animals came four by four.
   One more river to cross.
   The hippopotamus got stuck in the door.
   One more river to cross.

5. The animals came five by five.
   One more river to cross.
   The bees came swarming from the hive.
   One more river to cross.

Arithmetic Song
Charles J. Cromwell
Rhythmically
1 (do)
Danish Folk Tune
1. 13 ru - ta - ba - gas, 13 ru - ta - ba - gas,
2. 14 ru - ta - ba - gas, 14 ru - ta - ba - gas,
3. 15 ru - ta - ba - gas, 15 ru - ta - ba - gas,
13 ru - ta - ba - gas, buy now. 13 ru - ta - ba - gas,
14 ru - ta - ba - gas, buy now. 14 ru - ta - ba - gas,
15 ru - ta - ba - gas, buy now. 15 ru - ta - ba - gas,
13 ru - ta - ba - gas, 13 ru - ta - ba - gas, buy now.
14 ru - ta - ba - gas, 14 ru - ta - ba - gas, buy now.
15 ru - ta - ba - gas, 15 ru - ta - ba - gas, buy now.
7 and 13 make a score, Buy un - til I have no more.
(?) and 14 make a score, Buy un - til I have no more.
(?) and 15 make a score, Buy un - til I have no more.
13 ru - ta - ba - gas, 13 ru - ta - ba - gas,
14 ru - ta - ba - gas, 14 ru - ta - ba - gas,
15 ru - ta - ba - gas, 15 ru - ta - ba - gas,
13 ru - ta - ba - gas, buy now.
14 ru - ta - ba - gas, buy now.
15 ru - ta - ba - gas, buy now.
26

17
3
15

4. 16 rutabagas, 16 rutabagas, 16 rutabagas, buy now.
   (?) and 16 make a score, Buy until I have no more.
   16 rutabagas, 16 rutabagas, 16 rutabagas, buy now.
5. 17 rutabagas, 17 rutabagas, 17 rutabagas, buy now.
   (?) and 17 make a score, Buy until I have no more. etc.
6. 18 rutabagas, 18 rutabagas, 18 rutabagas, buy now.
   (?) and 18 make a score, Buy until I have no more. etc.
7. 19 rutabagas, 19 rutabagas, 19 rutabagas, buy now.
   (?) and 19 make a score, Buy until I have no more. etc.

In Denmark many stores sell vegetables by the score (twenty), just as we in this country sell a dozen eggs.

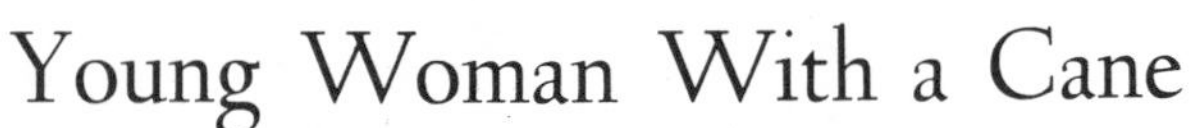

Young Woman With a Cane

Translated

Norwegian Folk Song

With accent
so (5)
1. Young wom-an with a cane · Lives up the moun-tain lane. ·
2. Young wom-an with a stick, · Jump right a-cross the creek. ·
3. Young wom-an with a cake, · She could-n't e - ven bake.
Half a pound of but - ter to a quart of cream,
If you'll cook the cof - fee, wa - ter will I bring;
All the cheese was mould-y and the cake was raw;
That's the rec - i - pe you al-ways use, it seems.
If you'll dance for me, I'll make my fid - dle sing.
And the knife was rust - y, could - n't cut or saw.
Young wom - an with a cane. ·
Young wom - an with a cane. ·
Young wom - an with a cane. ·

Walter de la Mare
Tired Tim
Sorrowfully
Marian Deere
do ti la
1. Poor tired Tim! · It's sad for him. · He lags the long bright morn-ing through, Ev - er so tired · of noth-ing to do; Poor tired Tim! · It's sad for him. ·
2. Poor tired Tim! · It's sad for him. · He moons and mopes the live-long day, Noth-ing to think a-bout, noth-ing to say; Poor tired Tim! · It's sad for him. ·
Old Nursery Rhyme
The Man in the Moon
Lightly
English
do (l)
G C G D7 G G7 C G D7 G
1. There · was a man lived in the moon, In the moon, in the moon, There · was a man lived in the moon, And his name was Man in the Moon-moon-moon.
2. And his hat was made of good cream cheese, Good cream cheese, good cream cheese, And his hat was made of good cream cheese, And his hat was made of · good cream cheese.
3. And his coat was made of good roast beef, Good roast beef, good roast beef, And his coat was made of good roast beef, And his coat was made of · good roast beef.

4. And his buttons were made of penny loaves,
Penny loaves, penny loaves,
And his buttons were made of penny loaves,
And his buttons were made of penny loaves.

5. And his vest was made of crust of pies,
Crust of pies, crust of pies,
And his vest was made of crust of pies,
And his vest was made of crust of pies.

Singing Games

Take hands, merry neighbors, for dancing the round!
Moonlight is fair and delicious the air;
From valley to valley our music shall sound.

William Allingham

All Around the Shu-Round

Mississippi Singing Game

Form a circle, holding hands. One girl in center.

5 (*so*)
5 (*so*) ♮4 (*fi*) 5 (*so*)

All a-round the shu-round, She wants to mar - ry, shu-round,
Circle shuffles to right, girl in center looks for a partner. (He)

Ain't got no part-ner, shu - round, Now get your part-ner, shu-round,
Girl in center chooses partner.

3 (*mi*) ♯2 (*ri*) 3 (*mi*)

Now back · to back, · shu-round, Now side · to side, · shu-round,
Dos-a-dos (back to back)
Catch left hands, shuffle sideways away from each other and back again.

Now face · to face, · shu-round, Now swing your part-ner, shu-round.
Drop hands, face partner.
Right elbow swing.
Girl returns to circle. Boy remains in circle and game continues.

Coffee Grows on White Oak Trees

Singing Game

Slowly
1 (do)
F
F
am
C7

Cof - fee grows on white oak trees, Riv - ers flow with sweet co - coa,

Form circle, face center, hands joined, move to right.

F
B♭
F
C7
F

Choose some-one to roam with you As sweet as strip - ed can - dy - o.

"Centers" choose partners.

quickly
F
F

1. Four in the mid - dle and you bet - ter get a - bout,

Four in center join hands, face outer circle, move right.

2. Eight in the mid - dle and your time's · most · out,

Same action as in first stanza.

C7
C7

Four in the mid - dle and you bet - ter get a - bout,
Eight in the mid - dle and your time's · most · out,

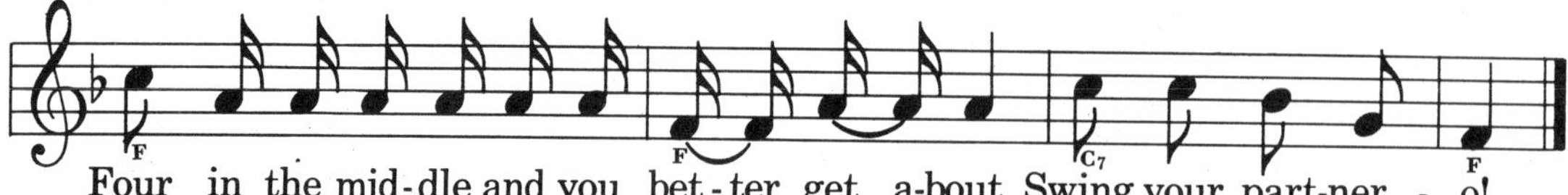
F
F
C7
F

Four in the mid-dle and you bet - ter get a-bout, Swing your part-ner - o!

All swing partners.

Eight in the mid-dle and your time's · most · out, Swing your part-ner - o!

Continue game until inner and outer circles are equal.

Put Your Little Foot

Couples stand side by side, boy slightly behind. Partners hold hands as shown in illustration.
Adapted
Varsovienne
so (5)
1. Put your lit - tle foot, put your lit - tle foot, put your lit - tle foot right down; Put your lit - tle foot, put your lit - tle foot, put your lit - tle foot right down.
To the left walk and turn, to the right walk and turn;
Left a - gain walk and turn, see how quick - ly we learn.
Point toe of left foot forward. Sweep it back over right instep.
Step leftward and slide right foot to meet left.
Repeat step.
Repeat step.
Turn right with weight on left foot.
Point right toe rightward.
Sweep right foot back over left instep.
Step rightward and slide left foot to meet right.
Repeat step.
Repeat step.
Turn left with weight on right foot.
Point left toe leftward.
Step, step, step.
Point right toe rightward.
Step, step, step.
Point left toe leftward.
Step, step, step.
Point right toe rightward.
Step, step, step.
Point left toe leftward.
G
D7
2. Oh, it's fun to dance, oh, it's fun to dance,
Oh, it's fun to dance with you;
Yes, it's fun to dance, yes, it's fun to dance,
Yes, it's fun to dance with you.
Sweep your foot, walk and point,
Sweep your foot, walk and point;
To the music so sweet,
Now this dance we'll repeat.

Shoo Fly

Singing Game

Single circles, of not more than eight to a circle, with hands joined. It is important that hands be joined firmly throughout the game.

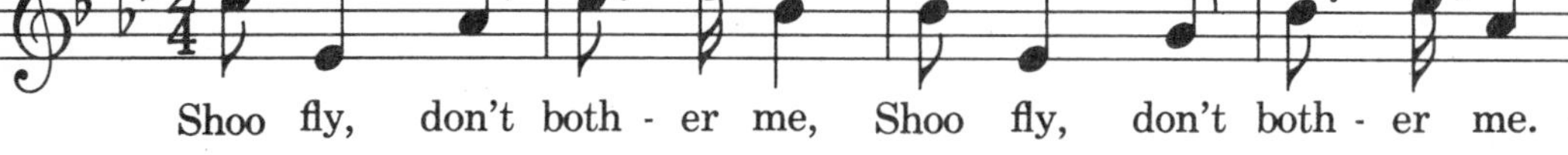
mi (3)
Shoo fly, don't both - er me, Shoo fly, don't both - er me.

(*Move forward, swinging arms upward to form a "teepee."*) (*Move backward, swinging arms downward.*)

Shoo fly, don't both - er me, For I be - long to some - bod - y. I

(*Repeat first action.*) (*Repeat second action.*)

do, I do, I do, And I will not tell you who; For

(*One couple form arch. Couple opposite arch lead group through it until the circle is turned inside out.*)
(*On repeat, reverse action.*)

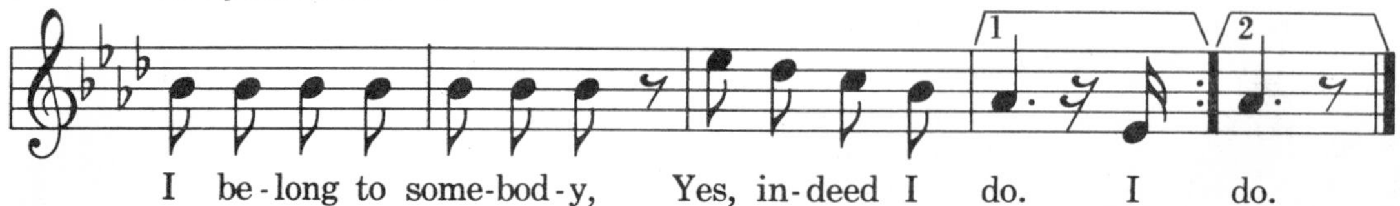
1 2
I be - long to some - bod - y, Yes, in - deed I do. I do.

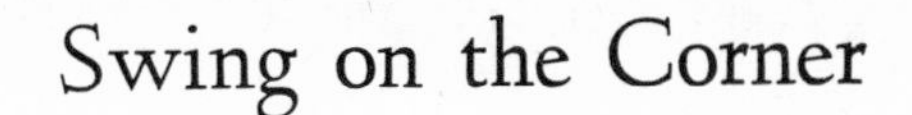

Swing on the Corner

Square Dance
1 (do)
1. First young cou - ple all a - round in · town, All a- round in · town, all a - round in · town; First young cou-ple all a- round in · town And bal - ance to your plac - es.
2. Take your part - ner and we'll all run a - way, We'll · all run a - way, we'll · all run a - way; Take your part-ner and we'll all run a - way And bal - ance to your plac - es.
Chorus
Swing on the cor - ner with a waltz and swing, With a waltz and swing, with a waltz and swing, Swing on the cor - ner with a waltz and swing And bal - ance to your plac - es.

3. Second young couple all around in town, *etc.*
4. Take your partner and we'll all run away, *etc.*
5. Third young couple all around in town, *etc.*
6. Take your partner and we'll all run away, *etc.*
7. Fourth young couple all around in town, *etc.*
8. Take your partner and we'll all run away, *etc.*

The directions for this dance are in your teacher's book.

Sweetheart Out A-Hunting

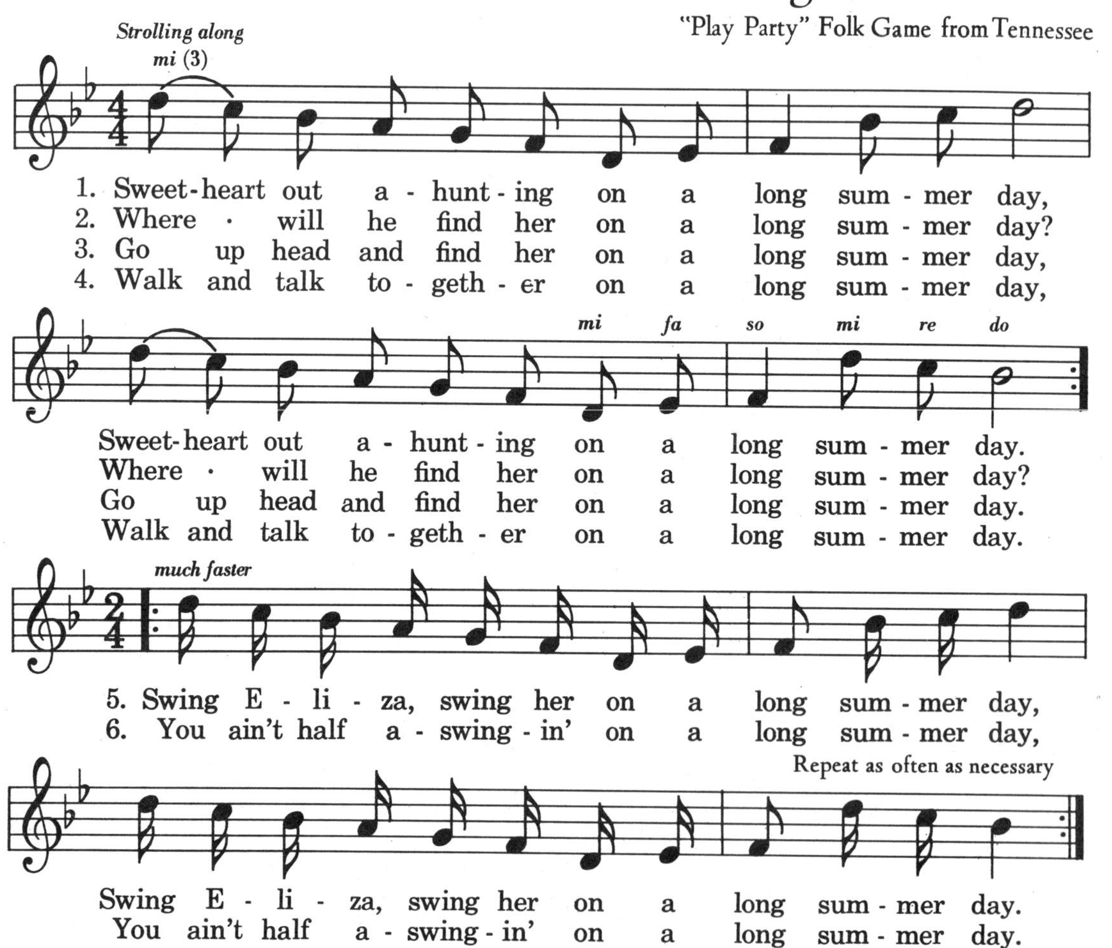
Strolling along
"Play Party" Folk Game from Tennessee
mi (3)
1. Sweet-heart out a - hunt - ing on a long sum - mer day,
2. Where · will he find her on a long sum - mer day?
3. Go up head and find her on a long sum - mer day,
4. Walk and talk to - geth - er on a long sum - mer day,
mi fa so mi re do
Sweet-heart out a - hunt - ing on a long sum - mer day.
Where · will he find her on a long sum - mer day?
Go up head and find her on a long sum - mer day.
Walk and talk to - geth - er on a long sum - mer day.
much faster
5. Swing E - li - za, swing her on a long sum - mer day,
6. You ain't half a - swing - in' on a long sum - mer day,
Repeat as often as necessary
Swing E - li - za, swing her on a long sum - mer day.
You ain't half a - swing - in' on a long sum - mer day.

Two lines, partners facing. Stanzas 1 and 2: boy of head couple strolls to foot of set and back to place.

Stanzas 3 and 4: head couple strolls to foot of set and back to place.

Stanzas 5 and 6: head couple locks right elbows and swings once and a half around. Head girl now locks left elbows with first boy in line and swings once around, while head boy does same with first girl in line. Then head couple locks right elbows and swings again in center, before proceeding to the next couple in line. This alternating action continues until head couple reaches foot of set. The game continues with new head couple.

Captain Jinks

Two lines, partners facing.

Traditional

do (1)

1. I'm Cap-tain Jinks of the Horse Ma-rines; I feed my horse on corn and beans.

(Clap hands, step forward, partners passing right shoulders.) *(Step backward to position.)*

2. I joined the ar-my when twen-ty-one; Of course I thought it lots of fun;
3. The first time I · went out to drill The bu-gle sound-ing made me ill;

I like the la - dies in their teens, For I'm the pride of the ar - my.

(Clap hands, step forward, passing left shoulders.) *(Step backward to position.)*

But from each bat - tle I did run, I'm not cut out for the ar - my.
Of bat - tle - fields I had my fill, I'm not cut out for the ar - my.

I teach young la-dies how to dance, · How to dance, · how to dance,

(Lock right elbows and swing.)

When I left home, Ma-ma, she cried, Ma - ma, she cried, Ma - ma, she cried,
The of - fi - cers, they all did shout, They all did shout, they all did shout,

I teach young la-dies how to dance, For that's the style in the ar - my.

(Lock left elbows and swing.)

When I left home, Ma-ma, she cried, "He's not cut out for the ar - my."
The of - fi - cers, they all did shout, "Let's put him out of the ar - my."

Chorus

Sa - lute your part - ner, turn to the right And swing your part - ner with all your might,

(Do as words say.)

And prom - e - nade a - round to the right, For that's the style in the ar - my.

Three Dukes

Traditional

1. Here come three dukes a - rid - ing, A - rid - ing, a - rid - ing,

"Ladies" look out window, see "Dukes" approaching, begin to powder faces, put on lipstick, arrange hair, smooth their skirts, etc. until words "ranson, pranson, tan-tan-ta-ra." At this point they form line facing "door" while pretending to blow horns.

Here come three dukes a - rid - ing, With a ran-son, pran-son, tan-tan - ta - ra!

"Dukes" enter "door" (down stage left) composed of two boys facing each other with hands joined and raised to form arch. "Dukes" come with high-stepping prancing gallop. They face line of girls on words, "ranson, pranson, etc." and pretend to blow horns. Throughout "Ladies" and "Dukes" pretend to blow horns on "ranson, pranson, tan-tan-ta-ra!"

2. Pray what is it you wish, Sirs,
You wish, Sirs, you wish, Sirs,
Pray what is it you wish, Sirs?
With a ranson, pranson, tan-tan-ta-ra!

"Ladies" advance toward "Dukes" with smiles and hands out in polite and welcoming gestures, then retreat to place in same manner.

3. Our wish, it is to marry,
To marry, to marry,
Our wish, it is to marry.
With a ranson, pranson, tan-tan-ta-ra!

"Dukes" advance toward "Ladies" with heads held high, bow stiffly, then retreat.

4. Will any one of us do,
Of us do, of us do,
Will any one of us do?
With a ranson, pranson, tan-tan-ta-ra!

"Ladies" advance smoothing skirts, touching their hair and smiling. They curtsey and retreat in the same manner.

5. Oh no, you're far too homely,
Too homely, too homely,
Oh no, you're far too homely.
With a ranson, pranson, tan-tan-ta-ra!

"Dukes" advance with "brushing off" movements of hands, heads shaking negatively and faces expressing scorn, then retreat in same manner.

6. We're quite as handsome as you are,
As you are, as you are,
We're quite as handsome as you are.
With a ranson, pranson, tan-tan-ta-ra!

"Ladies" advance tossing heads and wagging fingers at "Dukes" in a very saucy way, then retreat in same manner.

7. You're all as stiff as pokers,
As pokers, as pokers,
You're all as stiff as pokers.
With a ranson, pranson, tan-tan-ta-ra!

"Dukes" circle about, hands at sides, stepping stiffly and shrugging, first one shoulder, then the other as they look at "Ladies" with lifted eyebrows.

8. We can bend far better than you, Sirs,
Than you, Sirs, than you, Sirs,
We can bend far better than you, Sirs.
With a ranson, pranson, tan-tan-ta-ra!

"Ladies" dip and whirl about in a graceful dance ending in deep curtsies to the "Dukes."

9. We'll walk through the kitch - en and walk through the hall And

"Dukes" move right through kitchen "door" (formed by two girls) circling back of line of "Ladies," then through "door of hall." forming line as in beginning.

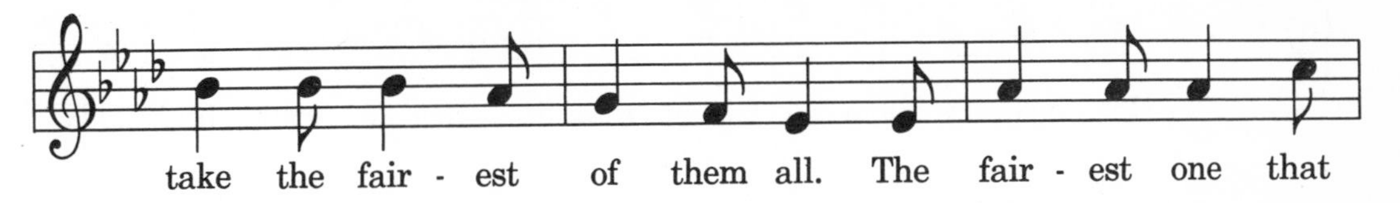

take the fair - est of them all. The fair - est one that

I can see Is pret - ty Miss Nell - ie. Come, dance with me.

Each "Duke" chooses a "Lady" who places her arm in his.

A procession, or any kind of dance, sung with "tra la la," etc. can end the play.

Dialogue and Dance Songs

The Bold Soldier

Not too fast
Traditional Ballad
so (5)
1. Sol - dier, O sol - dier that comes from the plain,
Court - ed a la - dy to hon - or and to fame.
Her beau - ty shone so bright that it nev - er could be told.
She al - ways loved a sol - dier be - cause he was so bold.
Chorus
Fa la la la · la la la la la, · Fa la la la · la la la la.

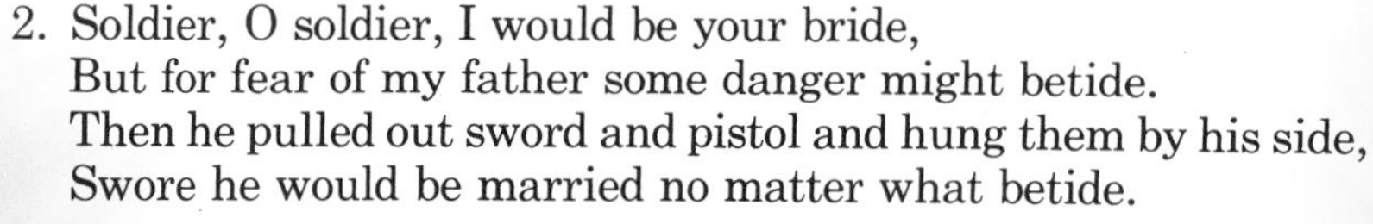
2. Soldier, O soldier, I would be your bride,
But for fear of my father some danger might betide.
Then he pulled out sword and pistol and hung them by his side,
Swore he would be married no matter what betide.

3. He took her to the parson and then home again.
There he met her father and seven armed men.
"Let us flee," said the lady, "I fear we shall be slain."
"Hold your hand," said the soldier, "and never fear again."

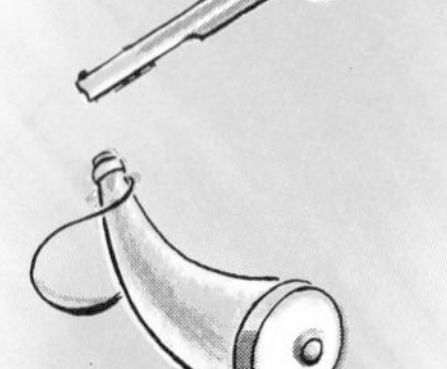

3 (mi)
G
C
D7
G

4. He pulled out sword and pistol and caus-ed them to rattle,
The lady held the horse while the soldier fought his battle.
"Hold your hand," said the old man, "and do not be so bold,
You shall have my daughter and a thousand pounds of gold."

The Brave Knight

Translated by Cecil Cowdrey

Italian Folk Song

At a moderate pace

1. See the brave knight in state ar - riv - ing!
2. Tell us what is the brave knight seek - ing?
3. For a love - ly young bride he's seek - ing.

From his moun-tains and from his val - leys.
From his moun-tains and from his val - leys.
From his moun-tains and from his val - leys.

G
C
D7
G

See the brave knight in state ar - riv - ing! A-yo-la, yo-la, yo - la.
Tell us what is the brave knight seek-ing? A-yo-la, yo-la, yo - la.
For a love - ly young bride he's seek-ing. A-yo-la, yo-la, yo - la.

4. Tell us, brave knight, how will you dress her?
From his mountains and from his valleys.
Tell us, brave knight, how will you dress her?
Ayola, yola, yola.

5. All in diamonds will we array her.
From his mountains and from his valleys.
All in diamonds will we array her.
Ayola, yola, yola.

6. Now indeed we are well content, sir.
From his mountains and from his valleys.
Now indeed we are well content, sir.
Ayola, yola, yola.

7. From the altar in state advancing
See the bride, ev'ry eye entrancing,
Hundred rings on her fingers glancing.
Ayola, yola, yola.

Flicka, Will You Dance With Me?

Translated by Luther Wilde

Swedish Folk Song

Moderately
so (5)
mi
re
fa
ti
1. Flic-ka,[1] will you come, will you come to the green? In all the mer-ry
2. Gos-se,[2] will you meet, will you meet me to - night? The moon is full and
scene You'll be the vil-lage queen. Oh yes, I will come for I am
bright And sheds a sil - ver light. Oh yes, I will meet you by the
glad of a chance To walk on the green, and to trip a coun-try dance.
old wish-ing well, For you are the one whom they call the vil - lage belle.
Fa bom fa de ral la, bom fa de ral la, bom fa de ral la la,
Fa bom fa de ral la, bom fa de ral la, bom fa de ral la la,
Fa bom fa de ral la la, fa bom fa de ral la la.
Fa bom fa de ral la la, fa bom fa de ral la la.
Oh yes, I will come for I am glad of a chance
Oh yes, I will meet you by the old wish - ing well,
To walk on the green, and to trip a coun - try dance.
For you are the one whom they call the vil - lage belle.

[1] *Flicka* = girl. [2] *Gosse* = boy.

Come, My Dove

Translated by Luther Wilde

Mexican Folk Song

Gracefully
mi (3)
1. Come, my dove, and dance the jo - ta,[1] All the vil - lage is danc - ing too;
2. If a girl dis - likes her part - ner, She will give the un - luck - y lad
I will be your sky - blue pi - geon While we sing cu - ru, cu - ru.
Blos-soms from a squash or pump-kin; This will make him ver - y sad.

Chorus
A la jo - ta, jo - ta, the mu - sic is en - tranc - ing,

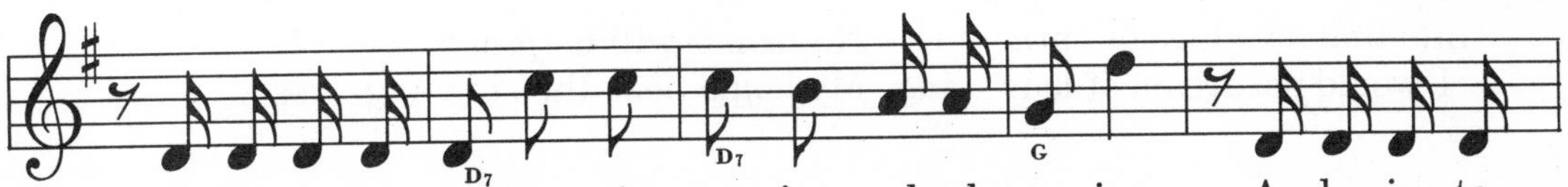
A la jo - ta, jo - ta, we're turn - ing and ad - vanc - ing, A la jo - ta,

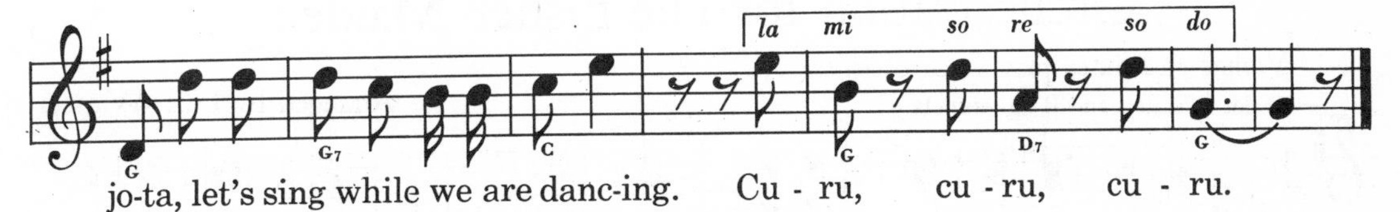
la mi so re so do
jo-ta, let's sing while we are danc-ing. Cu - ru, cu - ru, cu - ru.

[1] *Pronounce* ho´tah.

The Fisher Maiden

Translated by Carol Fuller

French Folk Song

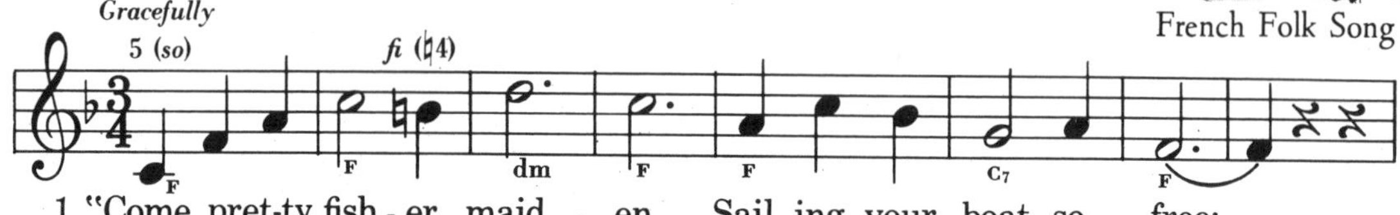

Gracefully
5 (so)
fi (♮4)
F F dm F F C7 F

1. "Come, pret-ty fish - er maid - en, Sail-ing your boat so free; ·
2. "No, no, no, no!" she an - swers, "I need no lace at all. ·

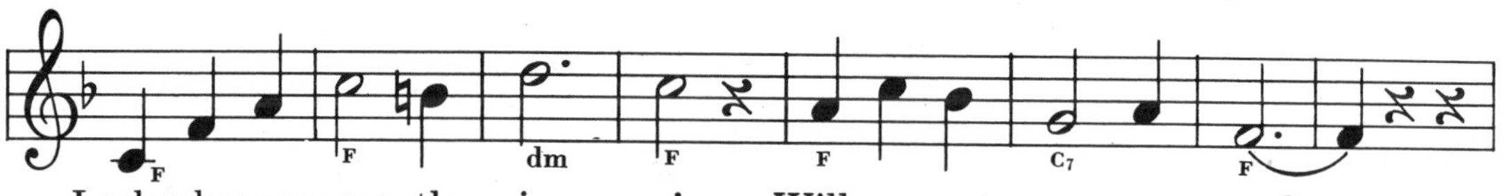

F F dm F F C7 F

Look where my cas - tle ris - es! Will you not mar - ry me? ·
Look how the foam is weav - ing Pat-terns that rise and fall. ·

C7 C7 F F G7 G7 C7

Blos-soms I'll bring, fresh as the spring; Ru - bies, lac - es I'll buy, ·
Sea-weeds that float close by my boat, Make a gar - den for me. ·

F F dm F F C7 F

Gifts that are glad sur - pris - es. No prince will be proud as I." ·
I would not dream of leav - ing My home near the shin - ing sea." ·

Orchestration for The Fisher Maiden

Violins and flutes play voice parts.

B flat Clarinets and B flat cornets

Arranged by L. E. Watters

E flat Altos and E flat saxophones.
Cellos, trombones and baritones.

Pay With a Smile

After the original by Ethel Crowninshield

Irish Folk Song

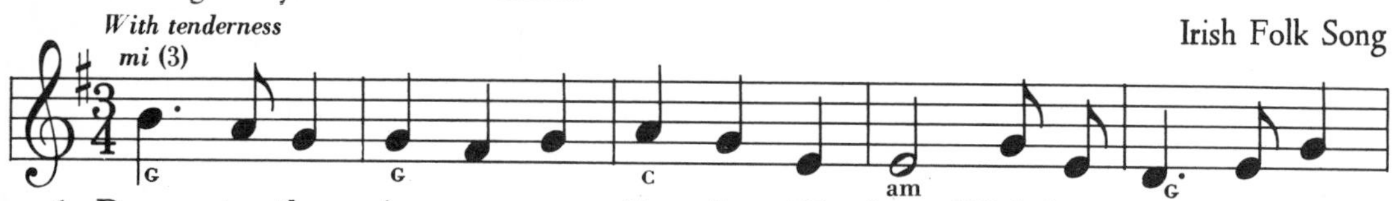

With tenderness
mi (3)
G
G
C
am
G

1. Down to the riv - er came lit - tle Ei - leen With her bright gold-en
2. "If you cross o - ver the riv - er to - day," Said the lad in the
3. "Blue are your eyes and your smile is so bright; Since you ask me to

G
A7
D7
G
G

hair like the crown of a queen. For it's o - ver the riv - er to
boat, "Why, you sure - ly must pay." "But I have - n't a pen - ny; I've
take you, I'm sure it's all right. So we'll hur - ry to mar - ket be-

C
A7
G
G
C
G

mar - ket she'd go, And she'll bring back a bun - ny that's white as the snow.
walked for a mile; Yet if you'll take me o - ver, I'll give you a smile."
fore it can rain, And per - haps, if you ask me, I'll take you a - gain."

There Grew a Rosy Maid

Translated by Christine Turner Curtis

Costa Rican Folk Song

With expression
mi (3)
F
C7
F
F

1. There grew a ros - y maid Dwell - ing in a rock - y glade.
2. The light of her blue eyes Shone like rays from sum - mer skies.

F
C7
C7
F
F

No fair - er maid was seen In pal - ace of a queen.
And though we're far a - part, She reigns with - in my heart.

CHORUS
And the warm and mel - low sun-shine of her glanc - es
On my path-way will glow wher - ev - er I go.

Mariquita

English version by Ann Rolfe

Folk Song from New Mexico

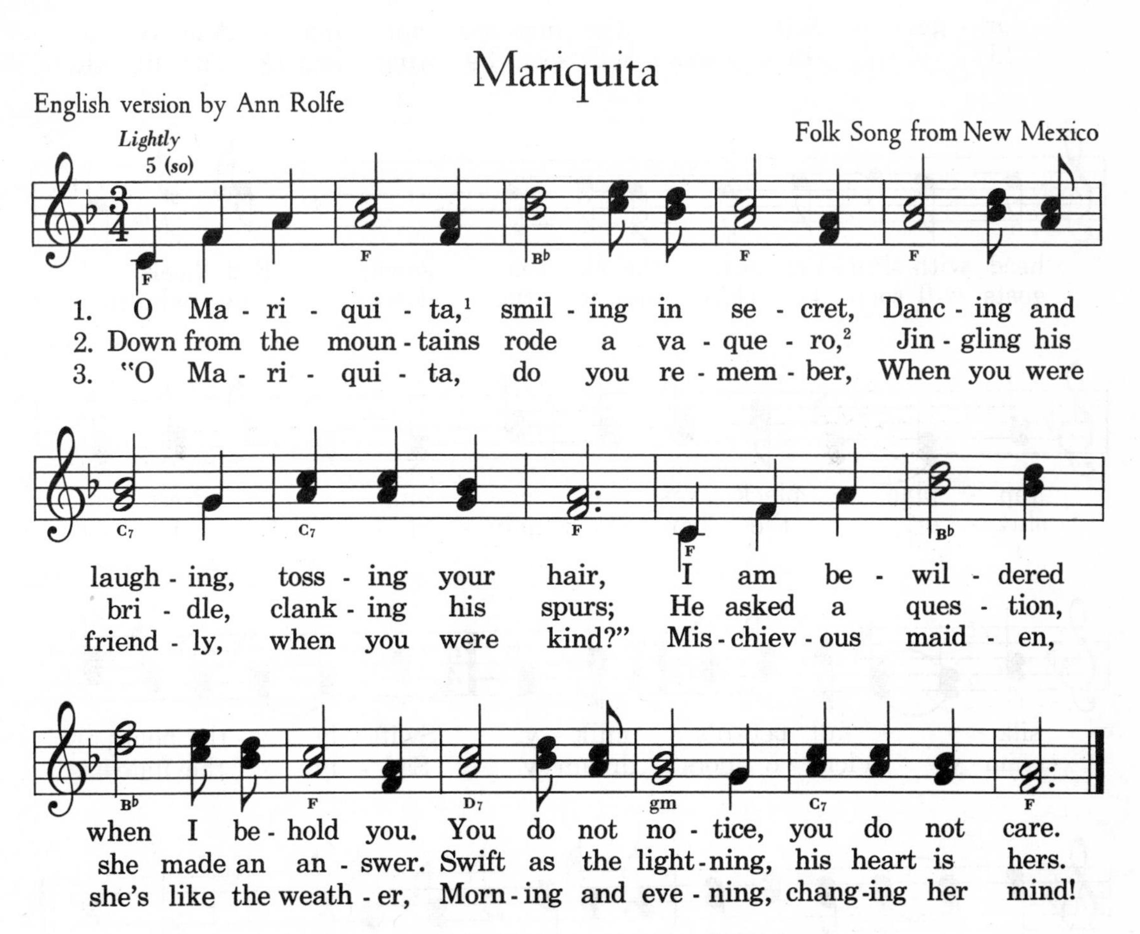
Lightly
5 (so)
1. O Ma - ri - qui - ta,[1] smil - ing in se - cret, Danc - ing and laugh - ing, toss - ing your hair, I am be - wil - dered when I be - hold you. You do not no - tice, you do not care.
2. Down from the moun - tains rode a va - que - ro,[2] Jin - gling his bri - dle, clank - ing his spurs; He asked a ques - tion, she made an an - swer. Swift as the light-ning, his heart is hers.
3. "O Ma - ri - qui - ta, do you re - mem - ber, When you were friend - ly, when you were kind?" Mis-chiev - ous maid - en, she's like the weath - er, Morn - ing and eve - ning, chang-ing her mind!

[1]*Pronounce* Mah ree kee'tah.

[2]*Pronounce* vah kay'ro. *Vaquero* is the Spanish word for cowboy.

In the Plaza

English version by Christine Turner Curtis
In tango rhythm
Mexican Folk Song
5 (so)
so mi fa so ti la
F F C7 C7 F F B♭ F C7 D7 C7 F C7 F F B♭ F C7 F
1. Sway-ing · be-neath the man-goes, Danc-ers · are weav-ing tan-goes; Soft-ly · the lutes are sigh-ing, · And o-ver-head with shin-ing stars the sky is sown. · Red heels are tap-ping, · black eyes are snap-ping; · On dress-es silk-y · fall pet-als milk-y. Swift-ly · the hours are fly-ing; · Too soon the balm-y night of sum-mer will be flown.
2. Crim-son, · in gar-dens hill-y, Blos-soms · the ti-ger lil-y. Pi-geons · will soon be wing-ing; · The lit-tle goats will soon be skip-ping in the dawn. · The palm trees shiv-er, · the ban-jos quiv-er, · Gar-de-nias cream-y · lend o-dors dream-y. Sad-ly · the flute is sing-ing; · Too soon the love-ly night of sum-mer will be gone.

Orchestration for In the Plaza

Violins and flutes play voice parts.
Arranged by L. E. Watters
B flat Clarinets.
B flat Cornets and trumpets.
Cellos, trombones and baritones.

Orchestration for In the Plaza (Continued)

E flat Altos and E flat Saxophones. (Saxophones may play an octave higher than written.)
Drums, castanets, tambourine, rhythm sticks, etc.

As I Went Walking Down the Street

Saucily
Texas Folk Song
1 (do)
C
G7
1. As · I went walk - ing down · the · street, 'Twas ·
2. "Where are you go - ing, my pret - ty lit - tle miss, Where
3. "Where do you live, · my pret - ty lit - tle miss, Where
4. "How · old are you, · my pret - ty lit - tle miss, How ·
on a moun - tain · grass - y, A · pret - ty lit - tle maid I ·
are you going, my · hon - ey?" She · an - swered me with a
do you live, my · hon - ey?" She · an - swered me with a
old are you, my · hon - ey?" She · an - swered me with a
chanced to meet Who an - swered · me so sas - sy.
tee - hee - hee, "I'm going to · hunt my mum - my."
tee - hee - hee, "I live on the hill with mum - my."
tee - hee - hee, "I'll be six - teen next Sun - day."
Chorus
The yad-dle ad-dle, ad-dle-um dai - sy; Yad-dle ad-dle, ad-dle-um,
yad-dle ad-dle, ad - dle-um; Yad-dle ad-dle, ad - dle-um dai - sy.

5. "Will you marry me, my pretty little miss,
Will you marry me, my honey?"
She answered me with a tee-hee-hee,
"I'll have to ask my mummy."

Sourwood Mountain

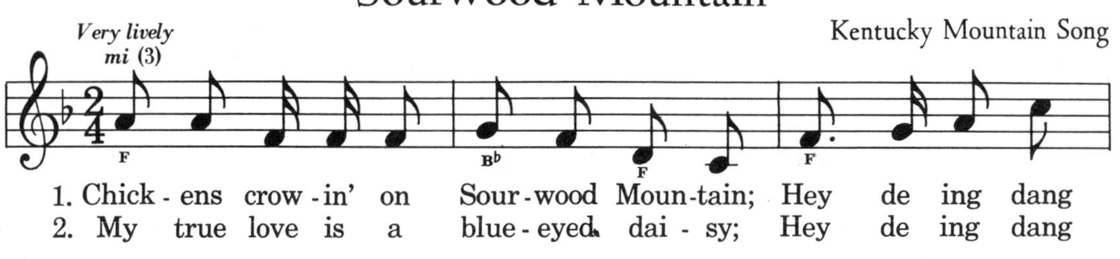
Very lively
mi (3)
Kentucky Mountain Song
F
B♭
F
F
1. Chick - ens crow - in' on Sour - wood Moun - tain; Hey de ing dang
2. My true love is a blue - eyed dai - sy; Hey de ing dang

C7
F
dm
gm
C7
dil - ly dal - ly day. So man - y pret - ty girls I can't count 'em;
dil - ly dal - ly day. She won't work and I'm too la - zy;

mi so la do la mi
F
C7
F
F
dm
Hey de ing dang dil - ly dal - ly day. My true love lives in the hol - low;
Hey de ing dang dil - ly dal - ly day. My true love lives up the riv - er;

F
C7
F
F
Hey de ing dang dil - ly dal - ly day. She won't come and
Hey de ing dang dil - ly dal - ly day. Few more jumps and

dm
F
C7
F
I won't fol - low; Hey de ing dang dil - ly dal - ly day.
I'll be with her; Hey de ing dang dil - ly dal - ly day.

I Wonder When I Shall Be Married

With humor
so (5)
do ti so
Folk Song
G
D7
D7
D7
1. I won - der when I shall be mar - ried, Be mar - ried, be mar - ried, I
2. My moth - er is read - y and will - ing, And will - ing, and will - ing, My
3. My shoes have gone to be mend - ed, Be mend - ed, be mend - ed, My

G
G
G
D7
G

won-der when I shall be mar-ried, · For my beau-ty's be-gin-ning to fade. ·
moth-er is read-y and will-ing, · For · she has four daugh-ters be-sides. ·
shoes · have gone to be mend-ed, · And my pet - ti - coat gone to dye green. ·

4. They're going to be ready by Sunday,
   By Sunday, by Sunday,
   They're going to be ready by Sunday.
   Oh say, won't I look like a queen?

At the Spinning Wheel

Translated by Cecil Cowdrey
Basque Folk Song
mi (3)
do (1)
1. Gai - ly my wheel turns round and round, Light as a sum-mer breeze.
2. Sail - or and farm-er crowd - ing by, Who says, "No time to lose?"
"Mar - ry," I hear them cry - ing, "Hur - ry, for time is fly - ing."
Two sail - ors half a pen - ny, mule driv - ers twice as man - y,
Sing - ing, I sit at ease. When I've a mind to take a
Who'd such a chance re - fuse? When I've a mind to take a
hus - band, I'll choose one where I please.
hus - band, I'll mar - ry whom I choose.

Listen to "Omphale's Spinning Wheel," Saint-Saëns.

Singing at Work

. . . all the workmen at their work,
All the seamen and the landsmen, . . .
Pioneers! O Pioneers!

Walt Whitman

Drill, Ye Tarriers

Thomas Casey

Charles Connolly

Ponderously, with heavy accent

la (6)

1. Ev - 'ry morn-in' at sev - en o'-clock There's twen-ty tar - ri - ers a - work - in' at the rock And the boss comes a - long and he

says, "Keep still and come down heav - y on the cast iron drill."

CHORUS

And drill, ye tar - ri - ers, drill, And drill, ye tar - ri - ers,

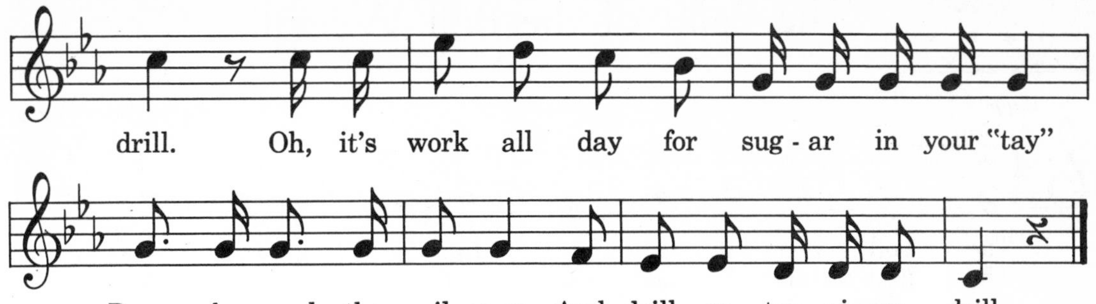
drill. Oh, it's work all day for sug - ar in your "tay"
Down be - yond the rail - way, And drill, ye tar - ri - ers, drill.

2. Our new foreman is Dan McCann.
I'll tell you sure he's a blame mean man,
Last week a premature blast went off
And a mile in the air went big Jim Goff.

3. Now the next time pay day comes around
Jim Goff was short one buck, he found;
"What for?" says he; then this reply,
"You're docked for the time you was up in the sky."

Work on the Railroad

Railroad Work Song

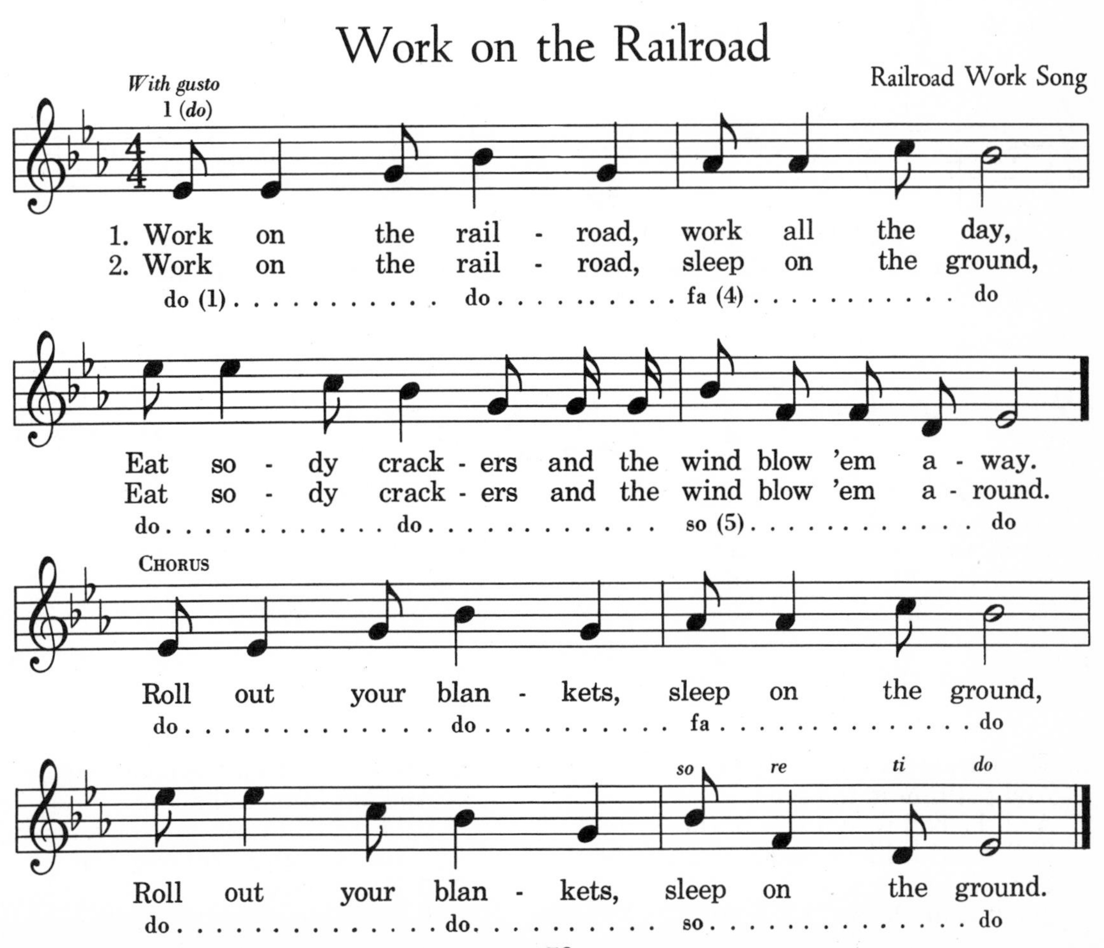
With gusto
1 (do)
1. Work on the rail - road, work all the day,
2. Work on the rail - road, sleep on the ground,
do (1) . . . . do . . . . fa (4) . . . . do
Eat so - dy crack - ers and the wind blow 'em a - way.
Eat so - dy crack - ers and the wind blow 'em a - round.
do . . . . do . . . . so (5) . . . . do
Chorus
Roll out your blan - kets, sleep on the ground,
do . . . . do . . . . fa . . . . do
so re ti do
Roll out your blan - kets, sleep on the ground.
do . . . . do. . . . . so . . . . do

The Ballit of the Boll Weevil

Happily
3 (mi)
Ballad from Texas
C
C
1. The boll wee - vil is a lit - tle black bug From -
2. The first time I see the boll · wee - vil He was
do (1) . . . . do . . . .

F
F
F
Mex - i - co they say, Come to try the Tex - as
sit - ting on the square; And the next time when I
fa (4) . . . . fa
fa . . . .

C
C
C
soil, · And he thought he'd bet - ter stay, Just a - look-ing for a
see him He had all his fam - i - ly there, Just a - look-ing for a
do . . . . do . . . . do . . . .

G7
G7
C
home, (Just a-look-ing for a home,) Just a-look-ing for a home. (Just a-look-ing for a home.)
home, (Just a-look-ing for a home,) Just a-look-ing for a home. (Just a-look-ing for a home.)
so (5) . . . . so . . . . do. . . . .

3. The farmer took the boll weevil
And put him in the sand;
And the boll weevil said to the farmer,
"I'll stand it like a man,
For it is my home,
For it is my home."

4. The farmer took the boll weevil
And left him on the ice;
Said the boll weevil to the farmer,
"This is mighty cool and nice,
It is my home,
It is my home."

'Leven-cent Cotton and Forty-cent Meat

Bob Miller and
Emma Dermer

In ballad style

do (1)
C
C
C
1. 'Lev-en-cent cot-ton and for-ty-cent meat, How in the world can a
2. 'Lev-en-cent cot-ton and for-ty-cent meat, How in the world can a

C
G7
C
C
poor man eat? Flour up high and cot - ton down low;
poor man eat? Mules in the barn, no crops laid by,

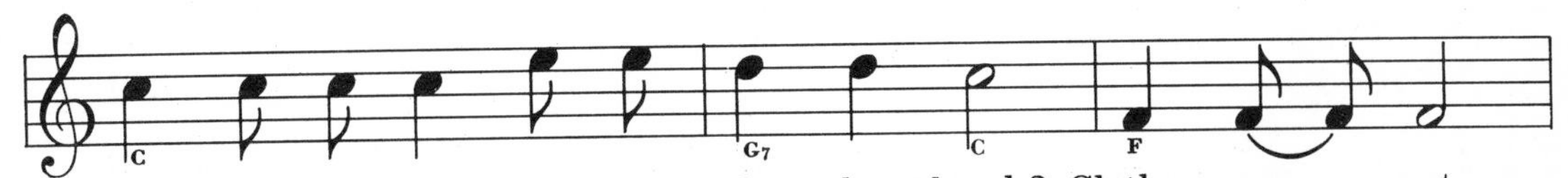
C
G7
C
F
How in the world can we raise the dough? Clothes worn · out,
Corn crib emp - ty and the cow's gone dry. Well wa - ter low,

fi (♯4)
C
D7
G
G7
shoes · run · down, Old slouch · hat with a hole · in the crown.
near - ly out of sight, Can't take a bath on · Sat - ur - day · night.

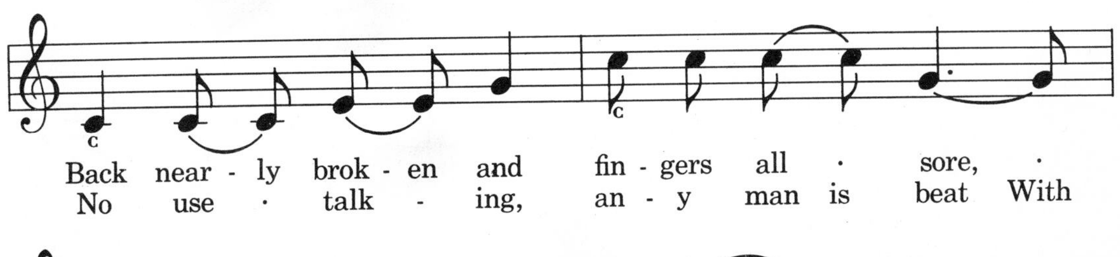
C
C
Back near - ly brok - en and fin - gers all · sore, ·
No use · talk - ing, an - y man is beat With

C
G7
C
Cot - ton gone down · to rise · no more.
'lev - en - cent cot - ton and for - ty - cent meat.

This song dates back to a period when the price of cotton was very low. People sing even when times are hard.

I'm a Roving Cowboy

Paraphrase from "Singing Cowboy"

With spirit

From "Singing Cowboy"

so (5)
G
G
G
D7
G

1. Oh, I'm a rov - ing cow - boy From off the West - ern plains;
2. Oh, come, you rov - ing cow - boys! You see I'm bound to roam.

G
G
G
D7
G

My trade is strap-ping sad - dles And pull - ing bri - dle reins.
I'm leav - ing my dear moth - er, Two sis - ters, and a home.

G
C
C
G

I can throw a las - so With speed and grace - ful ease,
Hear me, boys, a - shout - ing, "For - ev - er, young or old,

G
G
G
D7
G

And I can rope a bron - co, And ride him where I please.
I'll fol - low long-horned cat - tle: A life that's free and bold."

The Railroad Corral

Cowboy Song

Smoothly, with quiet enthusiasm
so (5) mi do la so mi
1. We're up in the morn - ing ere break - ing of day;
2. Come, take up your cinch - es, come, shake out your reins,
The chuck wag - on's bus - y, the flap - jack's in play.
Come, wake your old bron - co and break for the plains;
The herd is a - stir o - ver hill - side and vale,
Come, roust out your steers from the long chap - ar - ral,
With the night rid - ers crowd - ing them in - to the trail.
For the out - fit is off to the rail - road cor - ral.

3. The afternoon shadows are starting to lean
When the chuck wagon sticks in the marshy ravine.
The herds scatter farther than vision can look,
You can bet all true punchers will help out the cook.

4. But the longest of days must reach evening at last,
The hills now all climbed and the creeks now all passed;
The tired herd droops in the yellowing light,
Let them droop if they will, for the railroad's in sight!

Goin' to Leave Ol' Texas

Pensively
Cowboy Song
so (5)
1. I'm goin' to leave Ol' Tex - as now,
2. They've plow'd and fenc'd my cat - tle range,
1. I'm goin' to leave Ol' Tex - as
2. They've plow'd and fenc'd my cat - tle
They have no use for the long-horned cow.
And the peo-ple there are all so strange.
now, They have no use for the long-horned cow.
range, And the peo - ple there are all so strange.

3. I'll bid adios to the Alamo
And set my face toward Mexico.

4. I'll spend my days on the wide, wide range,
For the people there are not so strange.

5. The hard, hard ground will be my bed,
And the saddle seat will hold my head.

6. And when I waken from my dreams
I'll eat my bread and my sardines.

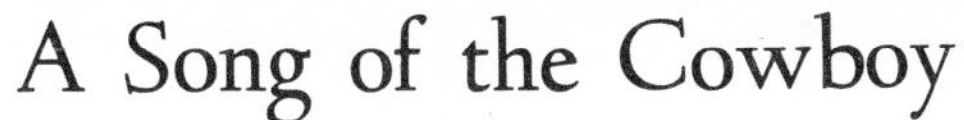

A Song of the Cowboy

George Hillers
Violin and flute.

Lulu Griesenbeck

Quietly
3 (mi)
C
G7
G7
F
C

1. Stars of the prai - rie skies Look down with shin - ing eyes.
2. Plain winds blow wild and cold; Wrapped in his blan - ket fold,

C
dm
G7
C

Here by the lone - ly fire A sleep - ing cow - boy lies.
Dream - ing of home and friends, He sleeps by em - bers gold.

C
dm
G7
C

Here by the lone - ly fire A sleep - ing cow - boy lies.
Dream - ing of home and friends, He sleeps by em - bers gold.

The Cowboy's Life

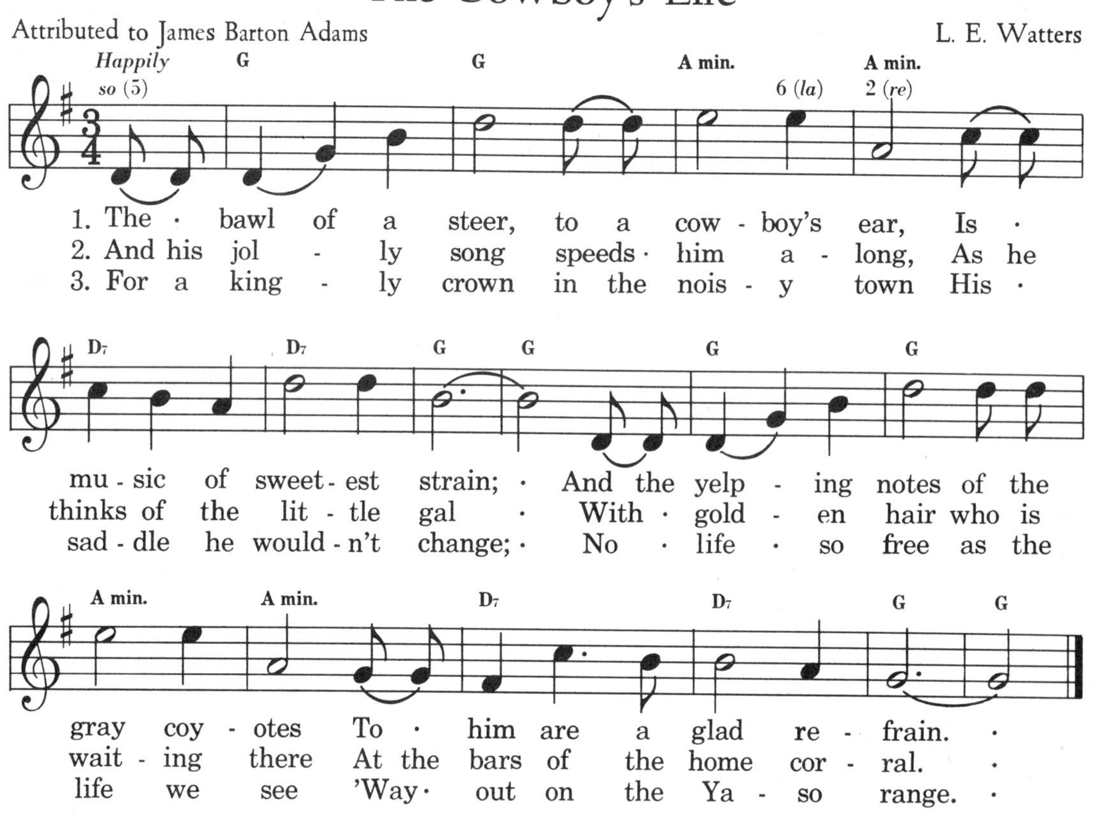
Attributed to James Barton Adams
L. E. Watters
Happily
so (5)
G
G
A min.
6 (la)
A min.
2 (re)
1. The · bawl of a steer, to a cow - boy's ear, Is ·
2. And his jol - ly song speeds · him a - long, As he
3. For a king - ly crown in the nois - y town His ·
D7
D7
G
G
G
G
mu - sic of sweet - est strain; · And the yelp - ing notes of the
thinks of the lit - tle gal · With · gold - en hair who is
sad - dle he would - n't change; · No · life · so free as the
A min.
A min.
D7
D7
G
G
gray coy - otes To · him are a glad re - frain. ·
wait - ing there At the bars of the home cor - ral. ·
life we see 'Way · out on the Ya - so range. ·

Round the Campfire

W. E.
5 (so)
3 (mi)
Walter Evans
F
Bb
F
C7
F
1. Round the camp - fire sing - ing, Sing - ing in har - mo - ny;
2. Round the camp - fire sing - ing, Sing - ing when day is done;
F
Bb
F
C7
F
Fire - flies gen - tly wing - ing, Night comes so si - lent - ly.
Cow - boy voic - es ring - ing, Rest comes for ev - 'ry - one.

Listen to "The Harmonica Player" (Bunkhouse Music), Guion. (Victor record.)

Eating Goober Peas
A. Pindar
P. Nutt
Merrily
mi (3)
la si (♯5) la
1. Sit - ting by the road - side · on a sum - mer day
2. When a horse - man pass - es the sol - diers have a rule To
3. Just be - fore the bat - tle the gen - 'ral hears a row, He
4. Now my song has last - ed · al - most long e - nough, The
Chat - ting with my mess - mates, · pass - ing time a - way,
cry out at their loud - est, · "Mis - ter, here's your mule."
says, "The Yanks are com - ing, · Hear their ri - fles now." He
sub - ject's in - ter - est - ing but rhymes are might - y rough, I
Ly - ing in the shad - ow · un - der - neath the trees.
But an - oth - er pleas - ure en - chant - ing - er than these Is
turns a - round in won - der. What do you think he sees? A
wish this war was o - ver, when free from rags and fleas, We'd
Good - ness, how de - li - cious eat - ing goo - ber peas.
wear - ing out your grind - ers eat - ing goo - ber peas.
band of Geor - gia sol - diers eat - ing goo - ber peas.
kiss our wives and sweet - hearts and gob - ble goo - ber peas.
Peas! Peas! Peas! Peas! Eat - ing goo - ber peas!
Good - ness, how de - li - cious, Eat - ing goo - ber peas!

"Goober peas" are really peanuts, and the people who originally sang this song must have liked them, judging by the cheerful mood of the music.

The song dates back to 1866, when it was first printed. It was very popular with the soldiers in the South during the war between the states.

The Erie Canal

Moderately with motion

Traditional American Ballad

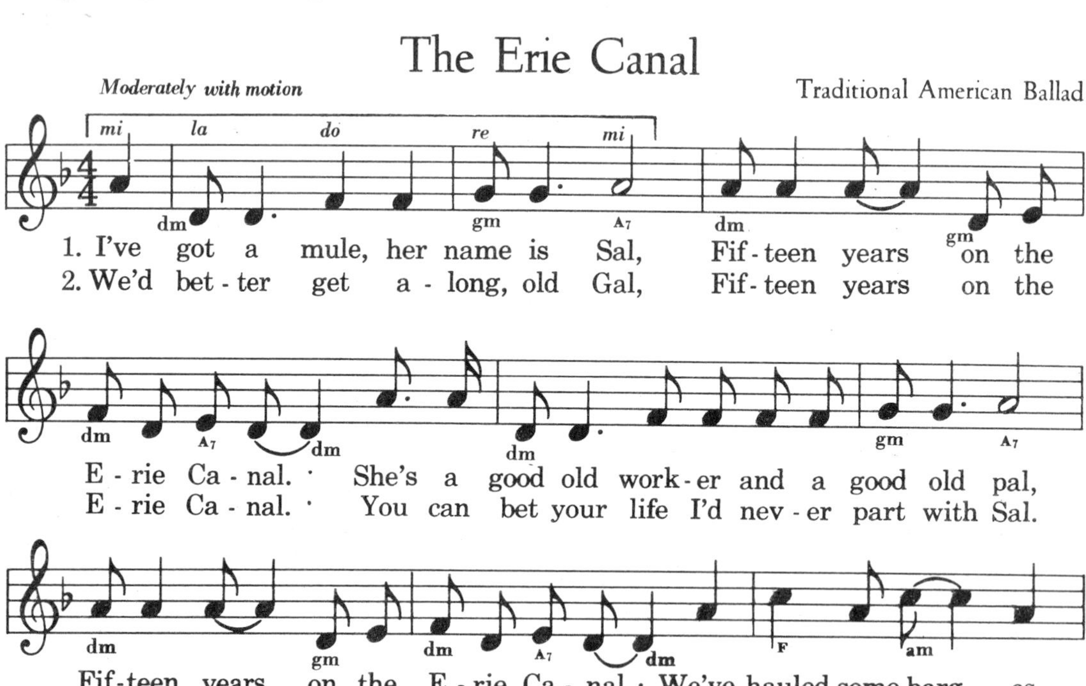

mi la do re mi
1. I've got a mule, her name is Sal, Fif-teen years on the
2. We'd bet-ter get a-long, old Gal, Fif-teen years on the
E-rie Ca-nal. She's a good old work-er and a good old pal,
E-rie Ca-nal. You can bet your life I'd nev-er part with Sal.

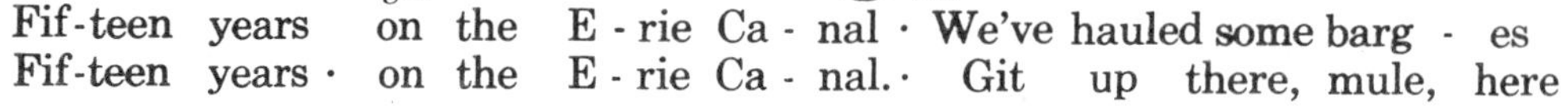

Fif-teen years on the E-rie Ca-nal We've hauled some barg-es
Fif-teen years on the E-rie Ca-nal. Git up there, mule, here

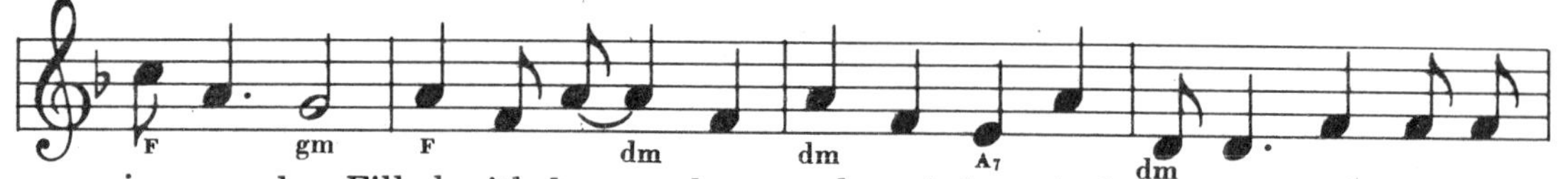

in our day Filled with lum-ber, coal and hay, And ev-'ry inch of the
comes a lock; We'll make Rome 'bout six o-clock. Just one more trip and then

way we know From Al-ba-ny to Buf-fa-lo.
back we'll go, Right back home to Buf-fa-lo.

CHORUS
Low bridge, ev-'ry-bod-y down! Low bridge for we're go-ing through a town.

And you'll al-ways know your neigh-bor, You'll al-ways know your pal

If you ev-er nav-i-gat-ed on the E-rie Ca-nal.

Don't Let Your Watch Run Down

American Folk Song

CHORUS
With spirit
mi (3)
Fine
Don't let your watch run down, Cap-tain, Don't let your watch run down.

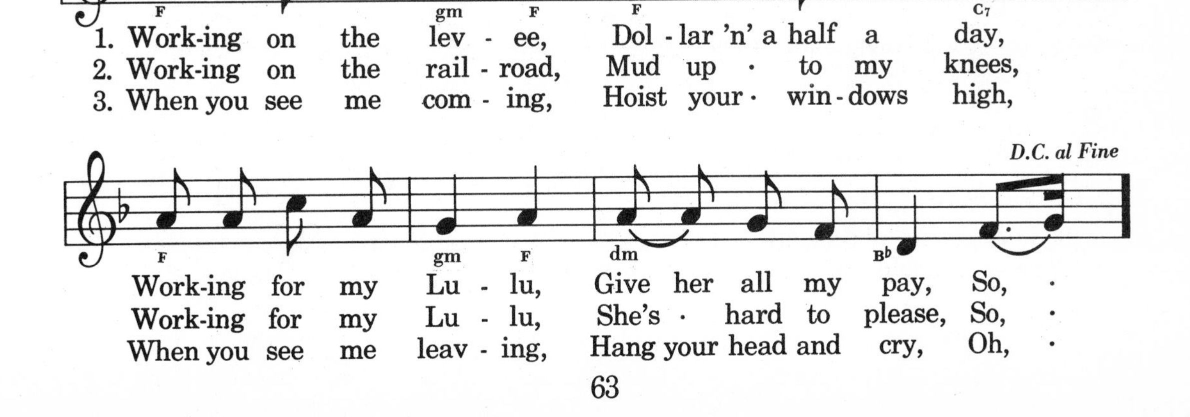
1. Work-ing on the lev-ee, Dol-lar 'n' a half a day,
2. Work-ing on the rail-road, Mud up to my knees,
3. When you see me com-ing, Hoist your win-dows high,
D.C. al Fine
Work-ing for my Lu-lu, Give her all my pay, So,
Work-ing for my Lu-lu, She's hard to please, So,
When you see me leav-ing, Hang your head and cry, Oh,

White waves heaving high, my boys,
The good ship tight and free—
The world of waters is our home,
And merry men are we.

Allan Cunningham

A Hundred Years Ago[1]

Sailor Chantey

Heartily
Solo
do (1)
Chorus
1. A hun-dred years is a ver-y long time, Ho, yes, ho!
2. They used to think that · pigs · could fly, Ho, yes, ho!
3. They thought the moon was · made · of cheese, Ho, yes, ho!
Solo
Chorus
A hun-dred years is a ver- y long time, A hun - dred years a - go.
I don't be-lieve it, · no, · not I, A hun - dred years a - go.
You can be-lieve it · if · you please, A hun - dred years a - go.

Listen to "The Flying Dutchman: Overture," Wagner.
How many of you can identify the "Sailors' Chorus" theme?

Cape Cod Chantey

Capstan Chantey

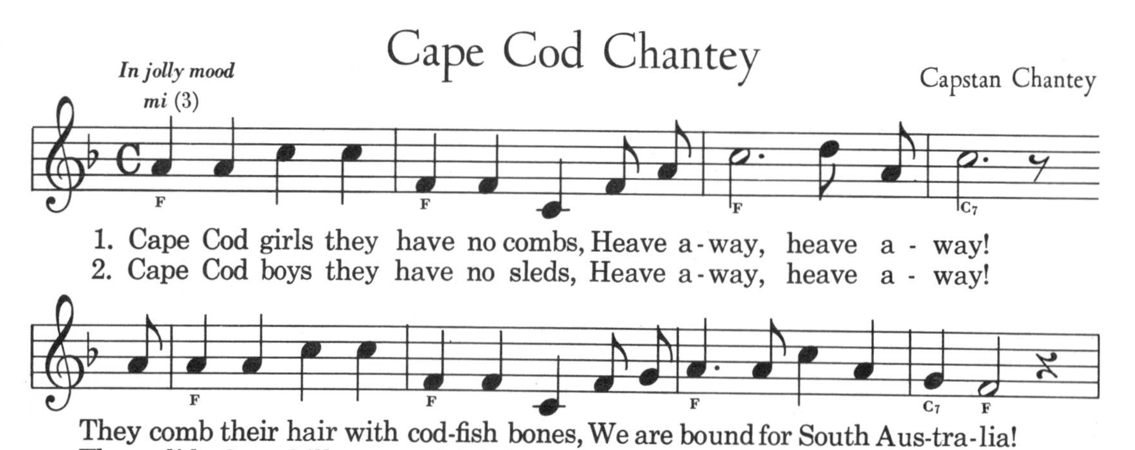
In jolly mood
mi (3)
1. Cape Cod girls they have no combs, Heave a-way, heave a - way!
2. Cape Cod boys they have no sleds, Heave a-way, heave a - way!
They comb their hair with cod-fish bones, We are bound for South Aus-tra-lia!
They slide down hill on cod-fish heads, We are bound for South Aus-tra-lia!

[1]From *Sailors' Songs or Chanties*, by Ferris Tozer. Used by permission of Boosey & Co. Ltd.

Heave a-way, my jol-ly, jol-ly boys, Heave a-way, heave a-way!
Heave a-way, and don't you make a noise, We are bound for South Aus-tra-lia!
B♭ F F F
B♭ F B♭ F C7 F

Listen to "Russian Sailor's Dance," from *The Red Poppy*, Gliere. (Columbia or Victor record.)

Fishermen's Evening Song
K. T. Sizer
Breton Air
Solo
Heartily
5 (so)
Chorus
1. One song, my com-rades, ere we go,
2. One cheer, my com-rades, ere we go,
3. One look, my com-rades, ere we go,
4. One pray'r, my com-rades, ere we go,
"Lis-ten to the glad waves' call!"
The tide runs high, the sun sinks low,
A Bre-ton fish-er fears no foe.
Our sea-port town lies safe and low.
For waves may roar and tem-pests blow,
"Lis-ten to the wild waves' call!"
We toil while oth-ers sleep,
'Mid rocks and whirl-pool's dread,
Sleep soft, dear friends at home,
Lord, let Thy strong arm be,
"Hark! they call, wild waves' call!"
Far sail-ing o'er the deep.
Bold-ly we seek our bread.
Sleep, while we cross the foam.
'Round all who toil at sea!
"Lis-ten to the deep waves' call!"

Nile Boatman's Song

Christine Turner Curtis

Egyptian Peasant Melody

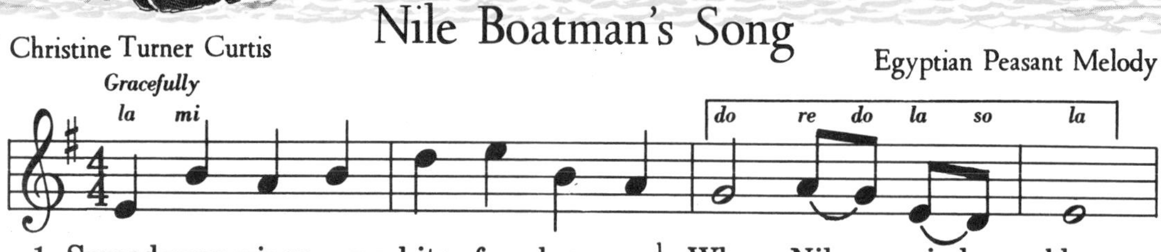
Gracefully
la mi
do re do la so la
1. Spread your wings, my white fe - luc - ca,[1] Where Nile · winds · blow;

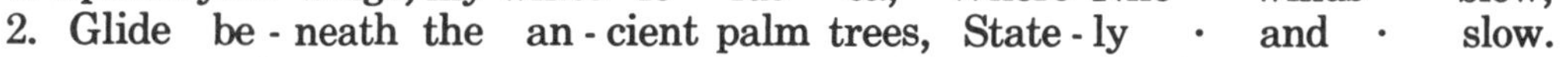
2. Glide be - neath the an - cient palm trees, State - ly · and · slow.

Sail by tem-ples of · great king-doms Van-ished long · a - go.
Sail be - side the fields of · cot - ton, Spread your wings like · snow.

[1] A boat with wing-like sails used on the Nile River.

The Blacksmith

Johann Ludwig Uhland
Translated

Johannes Brahms, Op. 19, No. 4

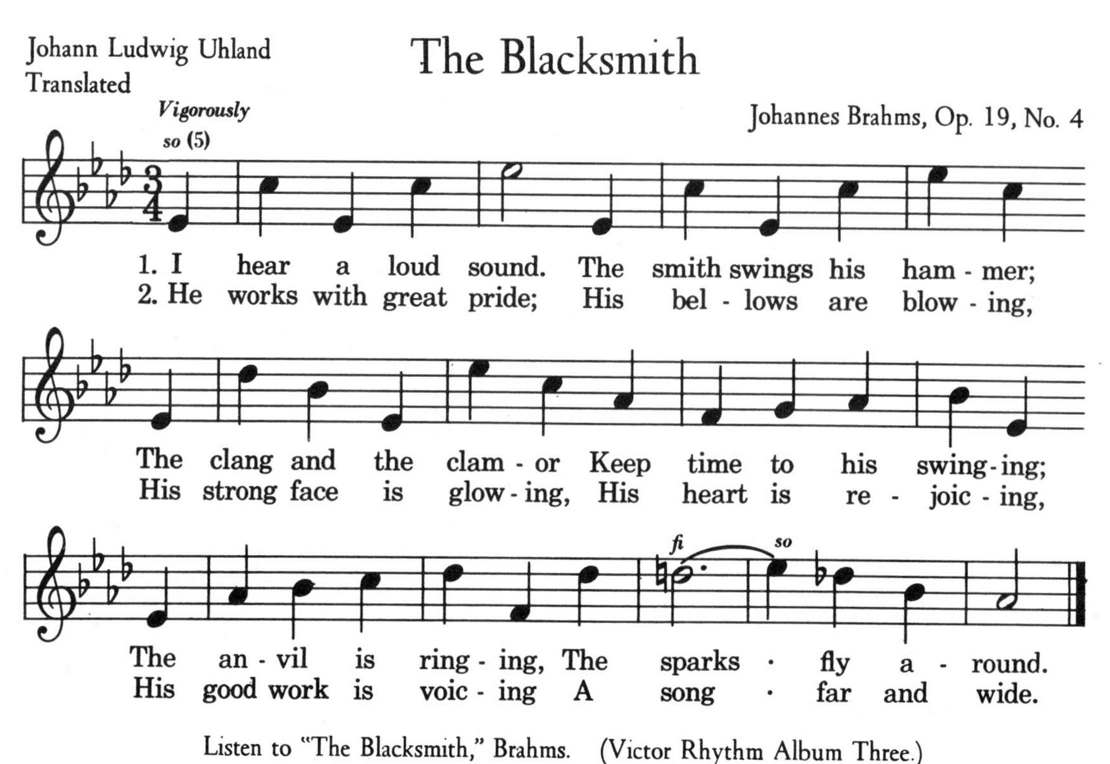
Vigorously
so (5)
1. I hear a loud sound. The smith swings his ham - mer;
2. He works with great pride; His bel - lows are blow - ing,
The clang and the clam - or Keep time to his swing - ing;
His strong face is glow - ing, His heart is re - joic - ing,
fi so
The an - vil is ring - ing, The sparks · fly a - round.
His good work is voic - ing A song · far and wide.

Listen to "The Blacksmith," Brahms. (Victor Rhythm Album Three.)

The Blacksmith Sings Merrily

Translated

German Folk Song

With accent
1 (do)
The black-smith sings mer - ri - ly, mer - ri - ly on, His
do (1) . . . . do . . . . .do. . . . . do
ham - mer and an - vil keep time to his song.
so (5) . . . . do . . . . so . . . . do
Cling, cling, clang, cling, cling, clang, cling, cling, clang, cling, cling, clang,
do . . . . do . . . . so . . . . do . . . .
Cling, cling, clang, cling, cling, clang, cling, clang, cling, clang.
do . . . . do . . . . so . . . . do

Some of you will enjoy playing the "chording" part on a B flat clarinet or a B flat cornet.

do (1)
so (5)

Listen to "The Anvil Chorus," from Il Trovatore, Verdi.

Buy My Flowers

María Gonzales

Entreatingly

F *mi* (3) *do* (1) — C

1. Oh, won't you buy my sweet gar - de - nias,
2. Oh, won't you buy them, se - ño - ri - tas,

C — F

My love - ly, fra-grant, white gar - de - nias?
These love - ly, fra-grant, white gar - de - nias?

F — C

Or would you rath - er buy ca - mel - lias?
Or, if you please, wear these ca - mel - lias.

C
F
D7

They're ros - y red or pink, so fair, And you can wear them in your
Ad - mir - ing glanc-es then will come. From fine se - ño - res they will

G min.
C7
F

hair. Please buy from me, *a - mi - gas mi - as.*
come. Please buy from me, *a - mi - gas mi - as.*

Past Three O'clock (Song of the Watchman)

James Fortescue
Tune "The London Waits" 17th Century
Chorus
do (1)
Past three o' - clock, and a cold and frost - y morn - ing;
Fine
Past three o' - clock, good mor - row, mas - ters all.
1. While in your beds you're peace - ful - ly sleep - ing,
2. We go the rounds, you rest at your lei - sure,
3. When morn - ing breaks, and slum - ber is end - ed,
D. C. al Fine
mi (3)
la (6)
Un - der the stars our watch we are keep - ing.
Safe is your house and safe is your trea - sure.
Give us your thanks, your homes who've de - fend - ed.

De Bezem (The Broom)

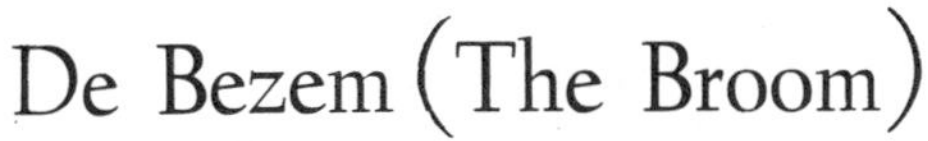

Dutch Round

1.
do (1)
2.
De be - zem, de be - zem, Wat doe je er mee? Wat doe je er mee?
The broom-o, the broom-o, What do you with it? What do you with it?

3.
4.
Wij ve - gen er mee, wij ve - gen er mee, De vloer aan, de vloer aan!
We sweep with it so, we sweep with it so, The floor up, the floor up!

Home and Family

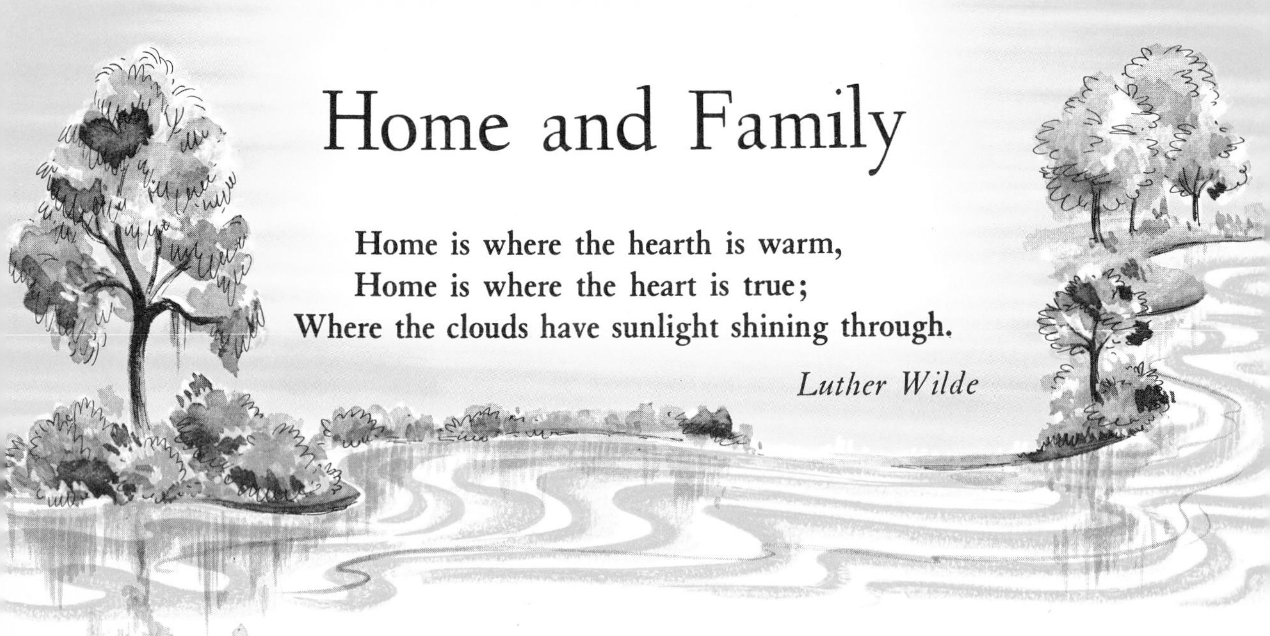

Home is where the hearth is warm,
Home is where the heart is true;
Where the clouds have sunlight shining through.

Luther Wilde

Old Folks at Home

Stephen Collins Foster

Moderately
mi (3)
Way down up-on the Swa-nee Riv-er, Far, far a - way,
All up and down the whole cre - a - tion Sad - ly I roam,
do (1). . . . . do . . . . fa (4). . . . .do . . . . so (5)
There's where my heart is turn-ing ev-er, There's where the old folks · stay.
Still long-ing for the old plan-ta-tion, And for the old folks at home.
do . . . . do . . . . fa . . . . do . . . . so . . . . do
CHORUS
All the world is sad and drear-y Ev - 'ry - where I roam;
so . . . . . so . . . . do . . . . . . do . . . . . fa . . . . fa. . . . . . do
O loved ones, how my heart grows wea-ry, Far from the old folks at home.
do . . . . do . . . . . . fa. . . . . do . . . . so. . . . . . . do

Memories

Christine Turner Curtis

Don Gardner

Expressively

so (5)
do (1)

1. When dusk is mov-ing down the sky, My thoughts go fly-ing west-ward
2. And I can see my moth-er look A-cross the mist-y rang-es.

To mem-'ries of a sun-set land Where pur-ple moun-tains loom.
I see her toss her gold-en head; Her cheeks are like the dawn.

I see a cot-tage sit-ting high A-bove the dust-y val-leys,
And clear-er than a moun-tain brook, I hear her joy-ous sing-ing,

A gar-den where the ros-es grow And moun-tain lil-ies bloom.
Like ech-oes of the thrush's song In sum-mers past and gone.

Peacefully, My Baby, Sleep

Alice Rose Denny

With quiet, flowing movement

Irish Cradle Song

1 (*do*)

1. Peace-ful-ly, my ba - by, . sleep, Stars in heav'n be - gin to peep;
2. Now the moon be - gins to · rise, Sail-ing through the peace-ful skies;

O'er thy bed of yel - low · gold, An-gels bright their wings un-fold.
'Mong the leaves her sil - ver · rays Shim-mer in the ee - rie haze.

Sho-heen sho, · loo la · lay, Birds of eve their ves - pers sing,
Sho-heen sho, · loo la · lay, Gen - tle Moth-er, Ma - ry mild,

Sho-heen sho, · loo la lay, With their hymns the val-leys ring. Sho-heen sho!
Sho-heen sho, · loo la lay, Through the night pro-tect my child. Sho-heen sho!

Listen to "Berceuse in D flat," Opus 57, Chopin. (Victor record.)

Old Gaelic Lullaby

Smoothly
mi (3)
Gaelic
dm gm dm dm dm gm A7

1. Hush! The waves are roll - ing in, White with foam, white with foam.
2. Hush! The winds roar hoarse and deep, On they come, on they come.

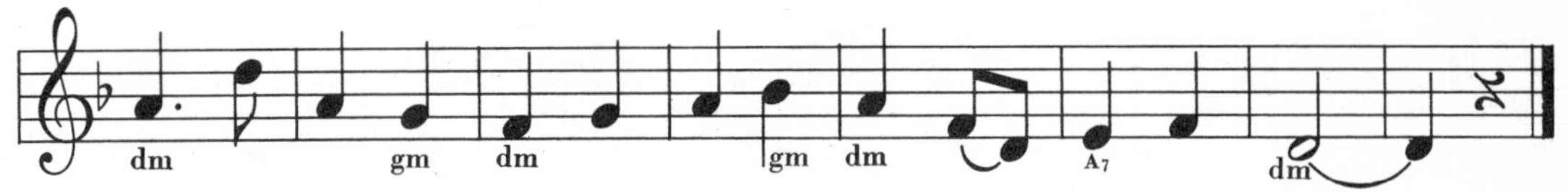
dm gm dm gm dm A7 dm

Fa - ther toils a - mid the din, But ba - by . sleeps at home. ·
Broth - er seeks the wan-d'ring sheep, But ba - by · sleeps at home. ·

Hush-A-By, Baby

Translated from Gaelic
With rocking motion
mi (3)
Ancient Scottish Lullaby
1. Hush - a - by, ba - by, my bon - nie wee lad - die,
2. Hush - a - by, dar - ling, and hush - a - by, dear - o,
When you're a man you shall fol - low your dad - die;
Hush - a - by, dar - ling will yet be a he - ro;
Bring me a cow and a goat from the heath - er,
None will be big - ger, or brav - er, or strong - er.
Bring - ing them home to your moth - er to - geth - er.
Lull - a - by, lit - tle one, cry - ing no long - er.

Slumber

Björnstjerne Björnson
English words by Auber Forestier
Halfdan Kjerulf
Tenderly
mi (3)
When ba - by's cheek pressed a
soft hand, in rest, Came an - gels that way, with
laugh - ter and play. When ba - by a - wak - ened, its

moth - er, guard keep-ing, Said, "Sweet- ly, my dar - ling, you
smile when you're sleep ing, When you're
sleep - ing."

Sleep, My Bonny, Blue-Eyed Little Treasure

Peacefully
5 (so)
3 (mi)
Lithuanian Folk Song
1. Sleep, my · bon - ny, blue - eyed lit - tle treas - ure,
2. May the · an - gels hov - er ev - er near thee,
Till the · ros - y dawn - ing of the day ·
Lov - ing · watch for - ev - er o'er thee keep; ·
Brings the hap - py hours of pleas - ure; Dream the star - ry
Sweet - est dreams will come to cheer thee, Sleep, my lit - tle
night a - way. · Sleep, · lit - tle treas - ure.
treas - ure, sleep. · Sleep, · lit - tle treas - ure.

Winkum, Winkum

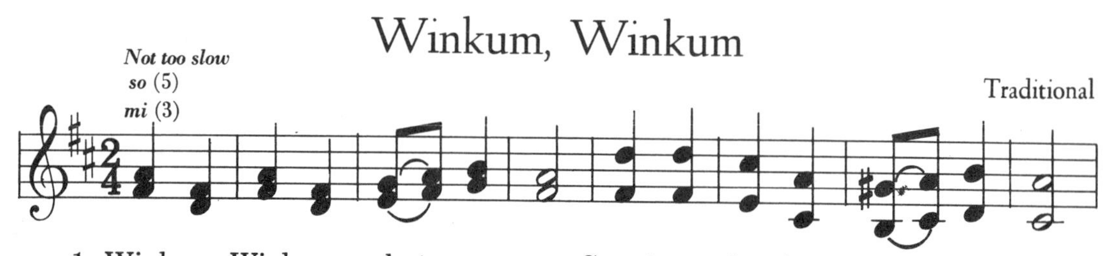
Not too slow
so (5)
mi (3)
Traditional
1. Wink-um, Wink-um, shut your eye, Sweet, my ba - by, lull - a - by,
2. Chick-ens long have gone · to rest, Birds lie snug with - in · their nest,

Listen to "Träumerei" (Dreaming), from *Scenes of Childhood*, Opus 15, No. 7, Schumann.

For the dews are fall - ing soft, Lights are flick-'ring up a - loft;
And my bird - ie soon will be Sleep - ing like a chick - a - dee;

And the moon-light's peep-ing o - ver Yon-der hill-top · capp'd with clo-ver.
For with on - ly half · a try, · Wink-um, Wink-um shuts her eye. ·

Karl Simrock
Translated
Lullaby and Good Night
With gentle motion
3 (mi)
1 (do)
Johannes Brahms
1. Lull - a - by and good night, with · ros - es be - dight, ·
2. Lull - a - by and good night, thy · moth - er's de - light, ·
With · lil - ies o'er - spread is · ba - by's wee bed.
Bright · an - gels be - side my · dar - ling a - bide.
Lay thee down now and rest, may thy slum - ber be blest;
They will guard thee from harms, thou shalt wake in my arms;
Lay thee down now and rest, may thy slum - ber be blest.
They will guard thee from harms, thou shalt wake in my arms.

Cradle Song

Sarojini Naidu
Francis Johnson Pyle
Slowly and quietly
1 (do)
1. From groves of spice, O'er fields of rice, A-thwart the lo - - tus stream, · I bring for you, A-glint with dew · A lit-tle love - ly dream, · A
2. Dear eyes, good night, In gold-en light The stars a-round you gleam; · On you I press With soft ca-ress · A lit-tle love - ly dream, · A
rit.
a tempo

lit-tle dream, A love-ly dream, A lit-tle, love-ly dream.
lit-tle dream, A love-ly dream, A lit-tle, love-ly dream.

Sleep, Sleep, My Darling
Tenderly
mi (3)
do (1)
French Lullaby
1. Sleep, sleep, my dar - ling, sleep peace-ful - ly, Moth - er is watch-ing, pray - ing for thee. May ho-ly an - gels, on wings of light, Bring to my ba - by dreams fair and bright. Do - do, my dar-ling, peace - ful - ly sleep.
2. Sleep, sleep, my dar - ling, sleep peace-ful - ly, Thy heav'n-ly Fa - ther car - eth for thee. In thy soft cra - dle peace-ful - ly sleep, While thou dost slum-ber, watch He will keep. Do - do, my dar-ling, peace - ful - ly sleep.

Slumber, Slumber

M. Louise Baum
Arthur B. Targett
With graceful rhythm
F mi (3) C7 F C7
1. Slum - ber, slum - ber,
2. Slum - ber, slum - ber,
do (1)
1. Slum - ber, my lit - tle one, Slum - ber, my pret - ty one,
2. Slum - ber so peace - ful - ly, Slum - ber so hap - pi - ly,
F D min. G min. G min. C7 C7
Float on the star - ry stream; Worlds of
Lift - ed be - yond the blue; Where the
Float on the star - ry stream; Worlds of all love - li - ness,
Lift - ed be - yond the blue; Where in the star-light the
F B♭ F C7 F F
won - der Fill your dream.
moon - boat Car - ries you.
won - der - ful world, Fill - ing your mag - i - cal dream.
moon is a boat Qui - et - ly car - ry - ing you.

Good Night to You All
Three-part Round
1. so (5)
Good night to you all and sweet be your sleep:
2.
May si - lence sur - round you, your slum - ber be deep:
3.
Good night, good night, good night, good night.
Good Night (Dobrou noc)
Translated by Rev. Vincent Pisek
Czech Folk Song
Slowly, with movement
mi (3)
Good night, be - lov - ed, good night, good night; God keep you safe in His
Good night, be - lov - ed, good night, good night; God keep you safe in His
watch - ful sight. Good night, dear, soft - ly sleep,
watch - ful sight. Good night, dear, dream of me,
Sweet be the dreams of your slum - ber deep. Good night, dear, soft - ly sleep;
And may your dreams ev - er pleas - ant be. Good night, dear, dream of me;

Sweet be the dreams of your slum - ber deep.
And may your dreams ev - er pleas - ant be. Good night, dear.

Songs of Worship
How Brightly Shines the Morning Star
Philip Nicolai
Translated
Nicolai-Bach
Joyously
do
How bright-ly shines the morn-ing star; Thy good-ness beam-ing from a - far,
All heav'n and earth re - joic - es. We sing Thy praise in joy - ful song,
And lift our hearts for - ev - er strong To praise thee with our voic - es.
Sing . out, ring . out mu - sic glo - rious, songs vic - to - rious,
Praise Thy glo - ry. Ev - er more our songs shall praise Thee.

Listen to "Fugue in C" (The "Fanfare" Fugue), Bach. (Victor record.)

Jacob's Ladder

Negro Spiritual

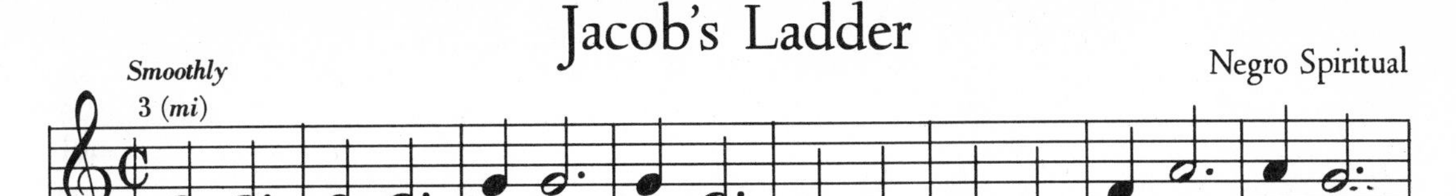

Smoothly
3 (mi)

1. We are climb-ing Ja-cob's lad-der, We are climb-ing Ja-cob's lad-der,
2. Ev-'ry round goes high-er, high-er, Ev-'ry round goes high-er, high-er,
3. We are climb-ing high-er, high-er, We are climb-ing high-er, high-er,

We are climb-ing Ja-cob's lad-der, Sol-diers of the cross.
Ev-'ry round goes high-er, high-er, Sol-diers of the cross.
We are climb-ing high-er, high-er, Sol-diers of the cross.

When Moses Smote the Water

Negro Spiritual

Happily
1 (do)
F
F
F
F

When Mo-ses smote the wa-ter, The chil-dren all passed o-ver,

Fine
F
F
F
C7
F

When Mo-ses smote the wa-ter, The sea gave a-way.

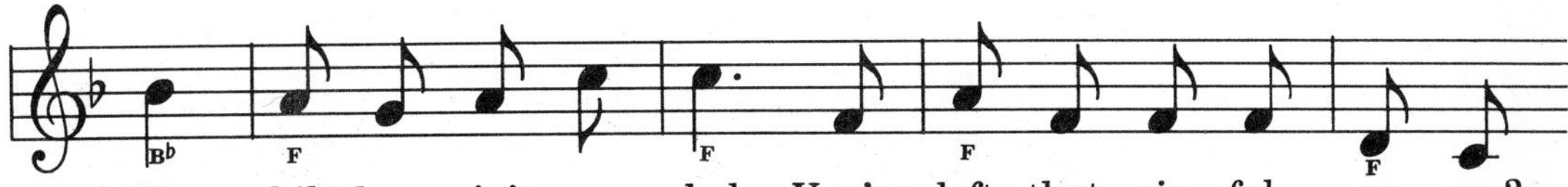

Bb
F
F
F
F

1. O chil-dren, ain't you glad You've left that sin-ful ar-my?
2. O broth-ers, ain't you glad You've left that sin-ful ar-my?

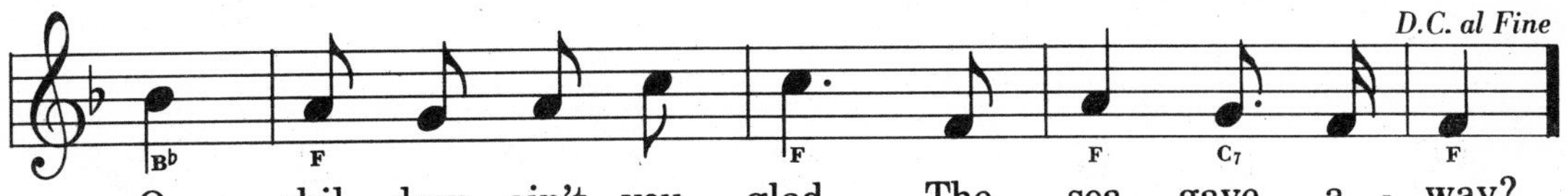

D.C. al Fine
Bb
F
F
F
C7
F

O chil-dren, ain't you glad The sea gave a-way?
O broth-ers, ain't you glad The sea gave a-way?

Goin' to Ride Up in the Chariot

With spirit
SOLO
mi (3)
CHORUS
Negro Spiritual

1. Goin' to ride up in the char - iot,
2. Goin' to meet my broth- er there, · Soon - er in the morn- ing.
3. Goin' to chat - ter with the an - gels,

SOLO
CHORUS

Ride up in the char - iot,
Meet my broth - er there, · Soon - er in the morn - ing.
Chat - ter with the an - gels,

SOLO
CHORUS

Ride up in the char - iot,
Meet my broth - er there, · Soon - er in the morn - ing, And I
Chat - ter with the an - gels,

hope I'll join the band. O Lord, have · mer - cy on me,

O Lord, have mer - cy on me; O Lord, have ·

mer - cy on me, And I hope I'll join the band.

There's a Little Wheel A-Turnin' in My Heart

Joyfully
do (1)
Negro Spiritual
1. There's a lit-tle wheel a-turn-in' in my heart, There's a lit-tle wheel a-turn-in' in my heart, In my heart, in my heart, There's a lit-tle wheel a-turn-in' in my heart.
2. There's a lit-tle song a-sing-in' in my heart, There's a lit-tle song a-sing-in' in my heart, In my heart, in my heart, There's a lit-tle song a-sing-in' in my heart.

3. Oh, I feel so very happy in my heart,
In my heart, in my heart,
Oh, I feel so very happy in my heart.

4. Oh, I feel like shouting in my heart,
In my heart, in my heart,
Oh, I feel like shouting in my heart.

Holy Spirit, Gift Divine

Paraphrase by Cecil Cowdrey

Reverently
la (6)
Basque Carol
1. Ho-ly Spir-it, gift di-vine, May our hearts Thy grace en-shrine: Com-fort bring, with gen-tle voice, Bid-ding anx-ious souls re-joice.
2. Guide us by Thy ho-ly might; Bless our eyes with Thy sweet light. Gift all oth-er gifts a-bove, With us bide, O per-fect love!

Faith of Our Fathers

Frederick W. Faber
Not too slow
mi (3)
Henri F. Hemy
1. Faith of our fa - thers, liv - ing still, In spite of dun - geon, fire · and sword; Oh, how our hearts · beat high · with joy When-e'er we hear that glo - rious word!
2. Our fa - thers, chained · in pris - ons dark, Were still in heart and con - science free; And bless'd would be · their chil - dren's fate If they, like them, should die · for thee!
3. Faith of our fa - thers, we · will strive To win all na - tions un - to thee; And through the truth · that comes · from God, Man-kind shall then in - deed · be free!
CHORUS
Faith of our fa-thers, ho - ly faith! We will be true to thee till death.

Orchestration for Faith of Our Fathers

Violins and flutes play the voice part.

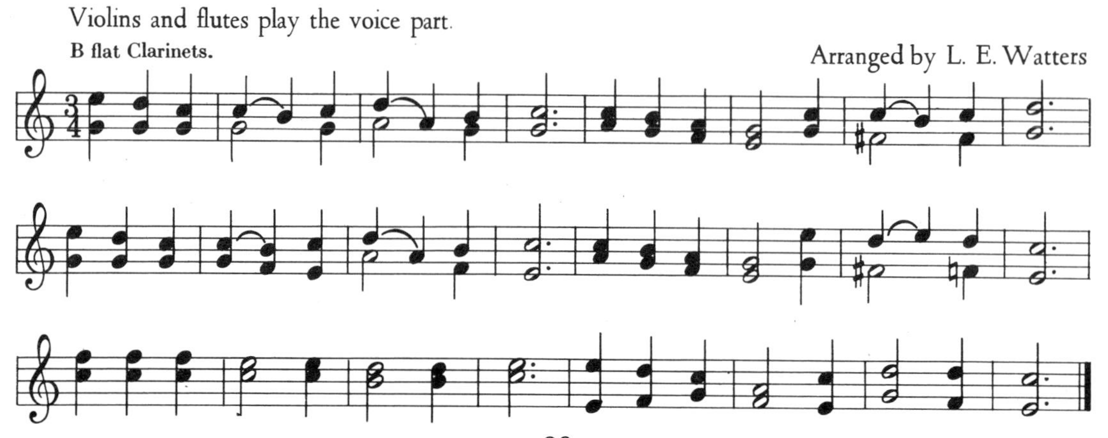
B flat Clarinets.
Arranged by L. E. Watters

B flat Cornets and trumpets.
E flat Altos (mellophones) and E flat saxophones.
Cellos, trombones and baritones.

Praise to the Lord

J. Neander, 1680

German, 1668

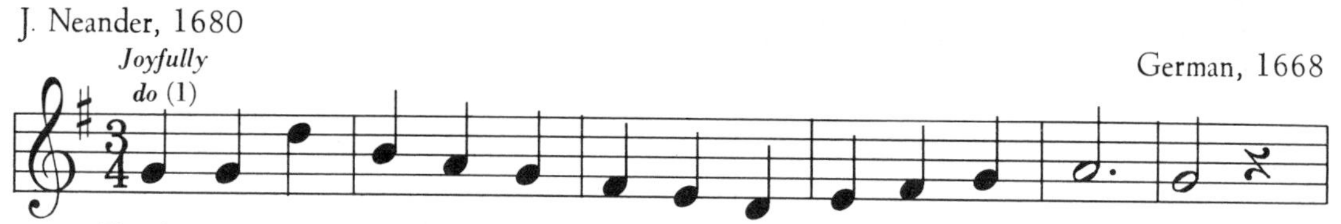
Joyfully
do (1)
1. Praise to the Lord, the Al - might - y, the King of cre - a - tion!
2. Praise to the Lord, Who o'er all things so won-drous - ly reign - eth,
3. Praise to the Lord! Oh, let all that is in me a - dore Him!

O my soul, praise Him, for He is thy health and sal - va - tion!
Shel - ters thee un - der His wings, yea so gen - tly sus - tain - eth.
All that hath life and breath, come now with prais-es be - fore Him!

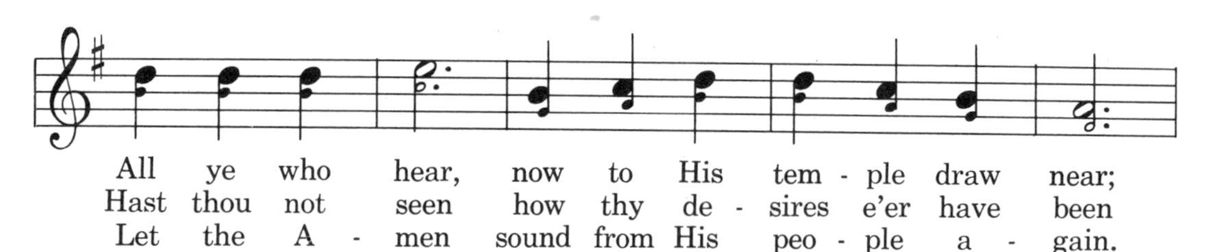
All ye who hear, now to His tem - ple draw near;
Hast thou not seen how thy de - sires e'er have been
Let the A - men sound from His peo - ple a - gain.

Join me in glad a - do - ra - tion.
Grant - ed in what He or - dain - eth?
Glad - ly for aye we a - dore Him.

But the Lord Is Mindful of His Own

From "St. Paul"

Felix Mendelssohn (Abridged)

Sweetly
so (5)
fi (♯4)
Fine
But the Lord is mind-ful of His own, · He re - mem-bers His chil-dren.

D.C. al Fine
But the Lord is mind-ful of His own, · The
Lord re-mem-bers His chil - dren, re-mem - bers His chil - dren.

Our Heavenly Father, Source of Love

Charles Wesley

Ludwig van Beethoven

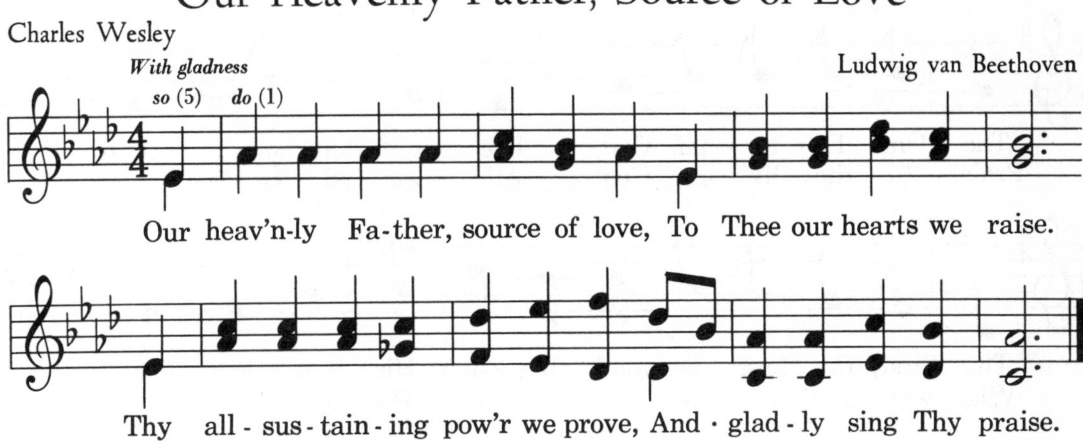
With gladness
so (5) do (1)
Our heav'n-ly Fa-ther, source of love, To Thee our hearts we raise.
Thy all - sus - tain - ing pow'r we prove, And · glad - ly sing Thy praise.

Hear Our Prayer, O Lord

George Whelpton

Quietly
3 (mi)
1 (do)
G D7 D7 G
Hear our pray'r, O Lord, Hear our pray'r, O Lord,
G G7 C G D7 G
In - cline Thine ear to us, And grant us Thy peace.

Praise to the Living God

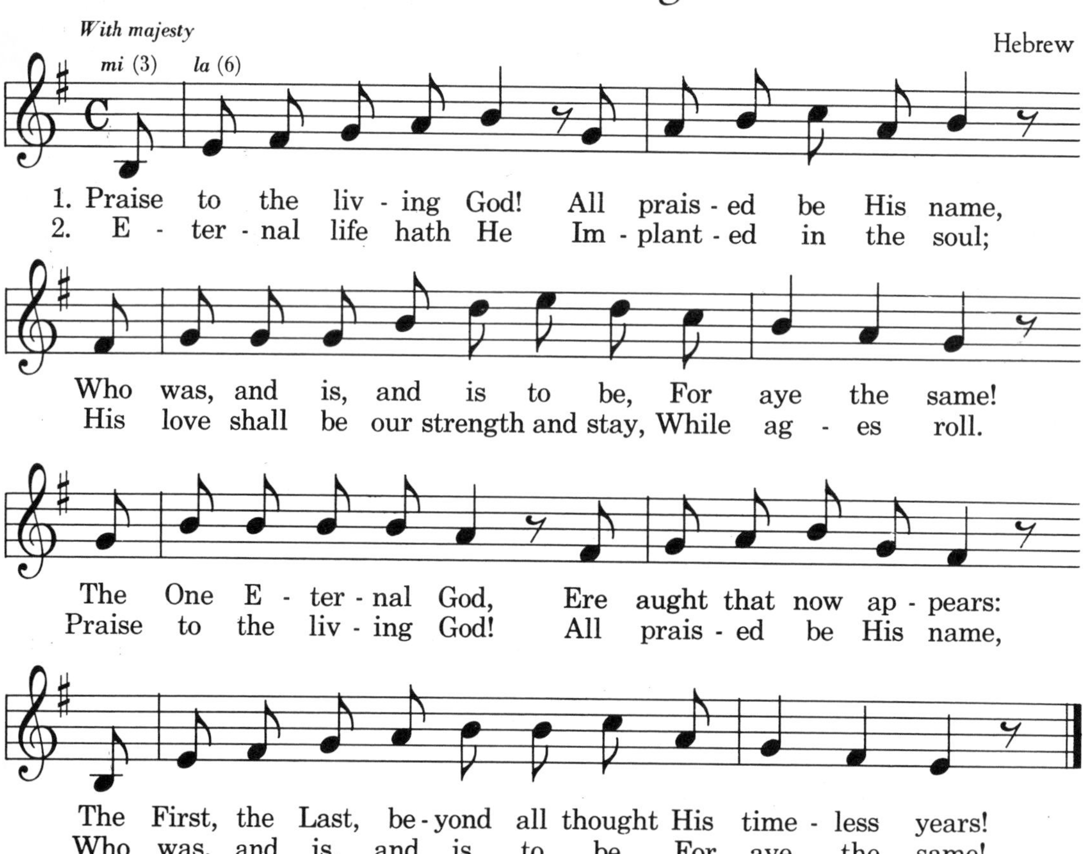
With majesty
Hebrew
mi (3) la (6)
1. Praise to the liv - ing God! All prais - ed be His name,
2. E - ter - nal life hath He Im - plant - ed in the soul;
Who was, and is, and is to be, For aye the same!
His love shall be our strength and stay, While ag - es roll.
The One E - ter - nal God, Ere aught that now ap - pears:
Praise to the liv - ing God! All prais - ed be His name,
The First, the Last, be - yond all thought His time - less years!
Who was, and is, and is to be, For aye the same!

Blessed Are the Pure in Heart

John Keble (Altered)

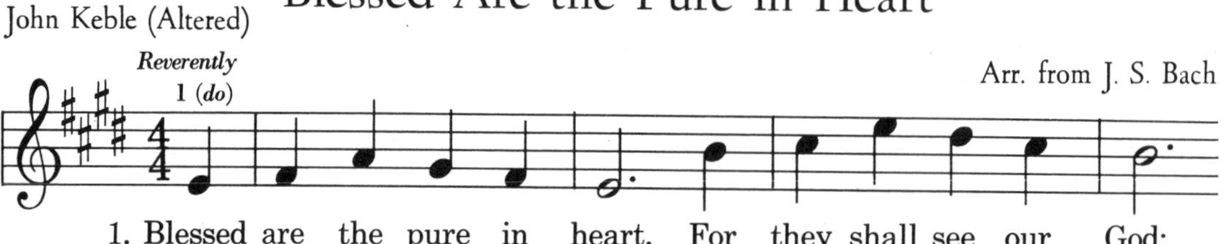
Reverently
Arr. from J. S. Bach
1 (do)
1. Blessed are the pure in heart, For they shall see our God;
2. He to the low - ly soul Doth still Him-self im - part,

3 (mi) ♯4 (fi) 5 (so)

The se - cret of the Lord is theirs, Their soul is God's a - bode.
And for His dwell-ing and His throne Choos-eth the pure in heart.

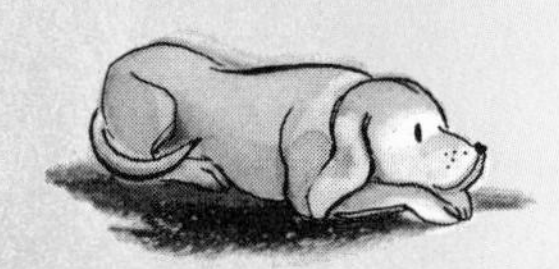

Songland People

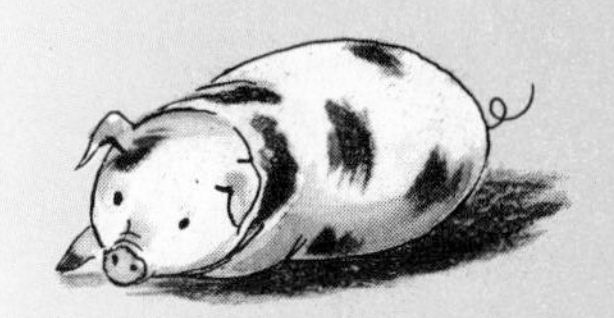

Sweet Betsy from Pike

Merrily
Pioneer Song
do (1)
1. Did you ev - er hear of sweet Bet - sy from Pike,
2. The al - ka - li des - ert was burn - ing and bare,
3. They swam the wide riv - ers and crossed the tall peaks,
do (1) . . . . .so (5). . . . . do. . . . . do
Who crossed the wide prai - ries with her hus - band Ike,
And Ike cried in fear, "We are lost, I de - clare!
They camped on the prai - rie for weeks up - on weeks;
do . . . . do . . . . so . . . . so
With two yoke of cat - tle and one spot - ted hog,
My dear old Pike Coun - ty, I'll go back to you."
They fought with the In - dians with mus - ket and ball;
do . . . . do . . . . fa (4) . . . . so
A · tall shang - hai roost - er, an old yal - ler dog?
Said · Bet - sy, "You'll go by your - self if you do."
They · reached Cal - i - for - nia in spite of it all.
do . . . . so . . . . do . . . . do
CHORUS
Sing too ra li oo ra li oo ra li ay,
do . . . . so . . . . do . . . . do
Sing · too ra li oo ra li oo ra li ay.
do . . . . so . . . . do . . . . do

Many friends whom we love best
Are those who live in songs.
Cindy[1]
With a saucy lilt
Southern Mountain Song
so (5)
1. I wish I was an ap - ple a - hang - in' in the tree,
do (1) . . . . do . . . . do . . . . so (5)
And ev - 'ry time my sweet-heart passed she'd take a bite of me.
do . . . . fa (4) . . . . so . . . . do
She told me that she loved me, she called me sug - ar plum,
do . . . . do . . . . do . . . . so
She throwed her arms a - round me, · I thought my time had come.
do . . . . fa . . . . so . . . . do
G
D7
C

[1]Copyright 1929 by Carl Fischer, Inc., New York. From *30 and 1 Folk Songs from the Southern Mountains,* compiled and arranged by Bascom Lamar Lunsford and Lamar Stringfield. Reprinted by permission.

CHORUS
Git a - long home, Cin - dy, Cin - dy, Git a - long home, Cin - dy,
fa . . . . fa . . . . do . . . .
Cin-dy, Git a-long home, Cin-dy, Cin-dy, I'll mar - ry you some-time.
do . . . . fa . . . . fa . . . . so . . . . do

2. You ought to see my Cindy, she lives away down South,
She's so sweet the honeybees swarm around her mouth.
The first time that I saw her she was standing in the door,
Her shoes and stockings in her hand and her feet all over the floor.

3. She took me to the parlor, she cooled me with her fan,
She swore that I's the purtiest thing in the shape of mortal man.
I wish I had a needle, as fine as I could sew,
I'd sew the girls to my coat tail, and down the road I'd go.

Mistress Shady

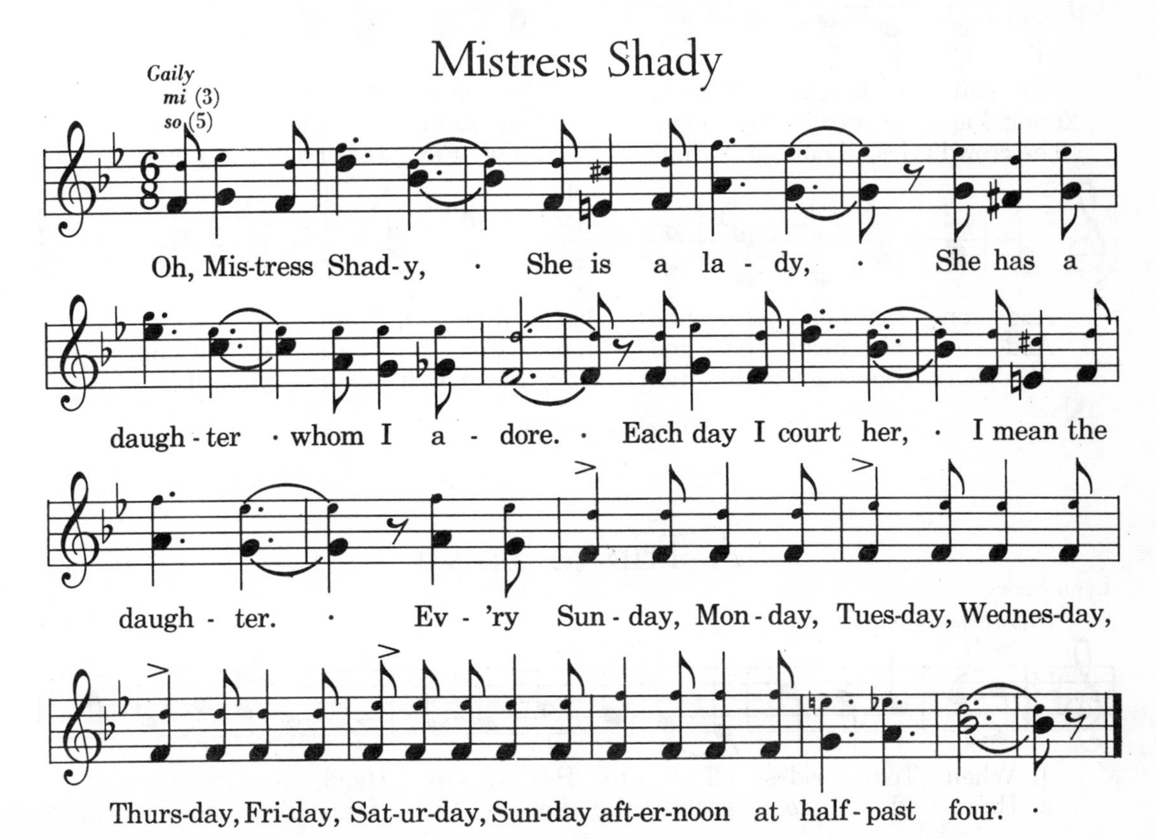
Gaily
mi (3)
so (5)
Oh, Mis-tress Shad-y, · She is a la - dy, · She has a
daugh - ter · whom I a - dore. · Each day I court her, · I mean the
daugh - ter. · Ev - 'ry Sun - day, Mon - day, Tues-day, Wednes-day,
Thurs-day, Fri-day, Sat-ur-day, Sun-day aft-er-noon at half - past four. ·

Pietro's Hat
After the original by Clara Louise Kessler
Playfully
do (1)
mi (3)
Italian Folk Song
1. Be - side the bus - y high - way Young Pie - tro¹ strolls a - long.
2. The pass - ers - by in won - der And ad - mi - ra - tion stare.
3. Just then the wind comes sweep-ing And blows his hat a - way,
He keeps his cane a - swing - ing And hums a lit - tle song.
"Who is this state - ly per - son Come out to take the air?"
And bobs and bumps and rolls it A - long the road in play.
His suit is bright and new, His shoes are shin - y too,
Young Pie - tro strolls a - long And hums his lit - tle song,
The crowd cries, "Look at that!" Young Pie - tro shouts, "My hat!"
And on his head a fine hat Just a bit a - skew.
And on his head the fine hat Fas - ci - nates the throng.
A horse comes down the high - way; Stamps it ver - y flat!
C
G7
F

[1]Pronounce pyā´trō.

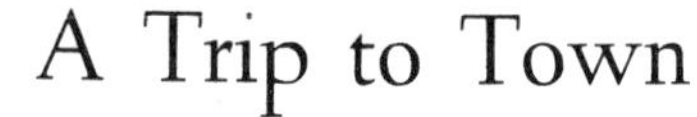

A Trip to Town

Lynn Seeley

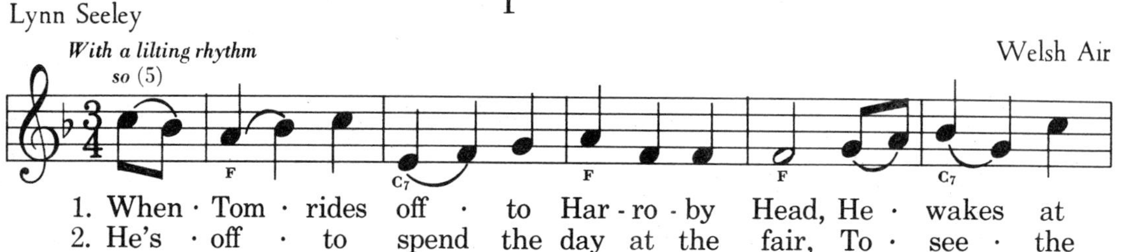
With a lilting rhythm
so (5)
Welsh Air
1. When · Tom · rides off · to Har - ro - by Head, He · wakes at
2. He's · off · to spend the day at the fair, To · see · the
F
C7

fi (♮4)
G7
C
C
B♭
C7
F

dawn · and leaps from his bed; He mounts his mare · and rides like the
cows · and sheep gath-ered there. He'll treat the girls · to can - dy and

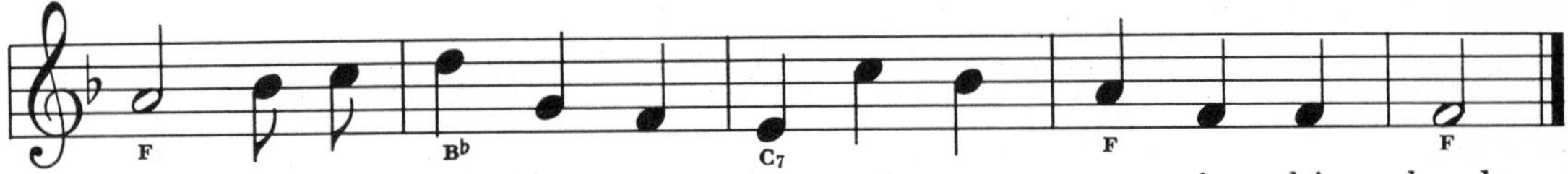

F
B♭
C7
F
F

wind; There's a dance in his toes and a tune in his head.
cake, If he feels in the mood and has pen - nies to spare.

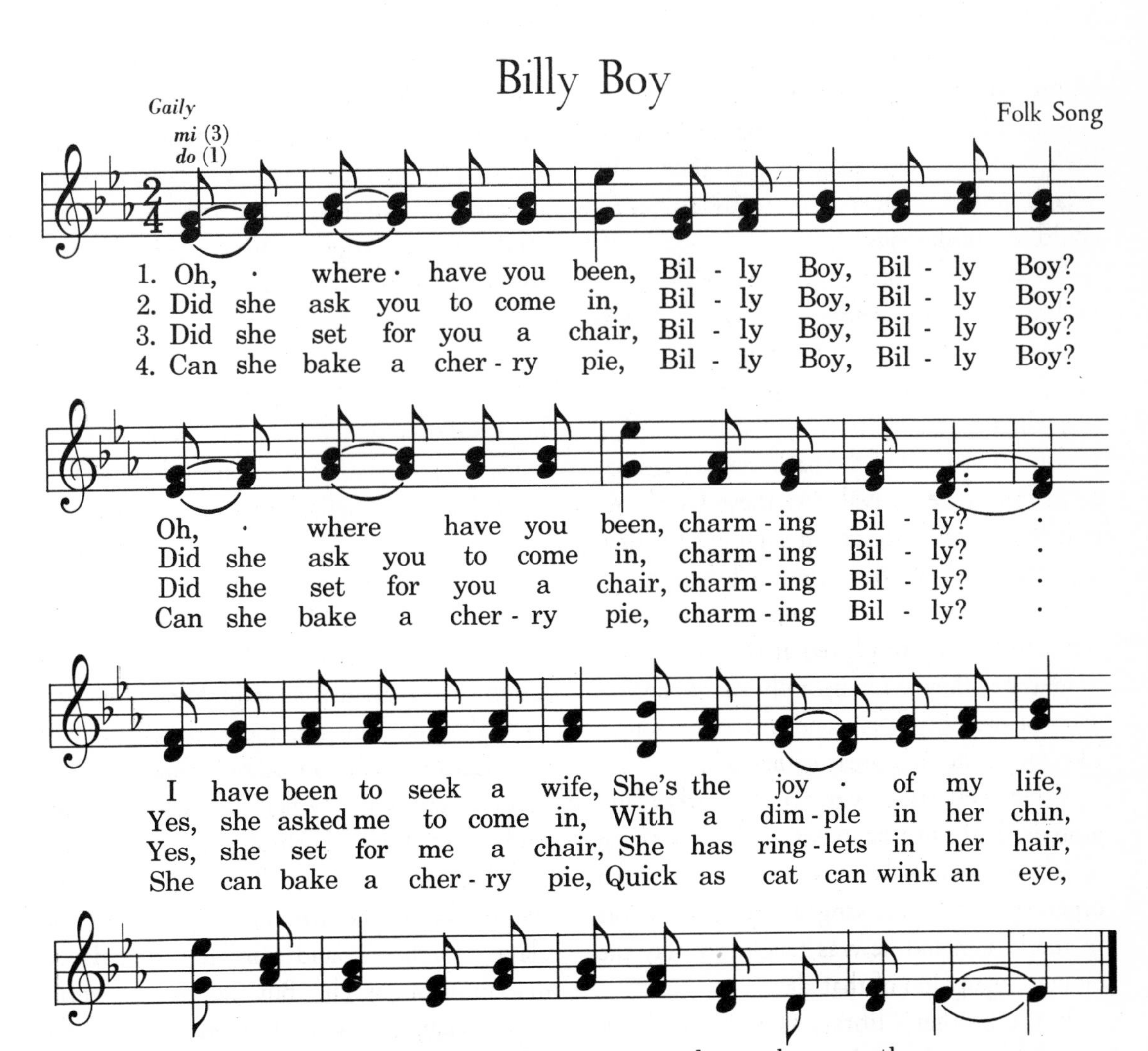

Billy Boy
Gaily
Folk Song
mi (3)
do (1)
1. Oh, · where · have you been, Bil - ly Boy, Bil - ly Boy?
2. Did she ask you to come in, Bil - ly Boy, Bil - ly Boy?
3. Did she set for you a chair, Bil - ly Boy, Bil - ly Boy?
4. Can she bake a cher - ry pie, Bil - ly Boy, Bil - ly Boy?
Oh, · where have you been, charm - ing Bil - ly? ·
Did she ask you to come in, charm - ing Bil - ly? ·
Did she set for you a chair, charm - ing Bil - ly? ·
Can she bake a cher - ry pie, charm - ing Bil - ly? ·
I have been to seek a wife, She's the joy · of my life,
Yes, she asked me to come in, With a dim - ple in her chin,
Yes, she set for me a chair, She has ring - lets in her hair,
She can bake a cher - ry pie, Quick as cat can wink an eye,
1,2,3,4. She's a young thing and can - not leave her moth - er. ·

There are magical names in the history of humanity—names that are like shaken lights or sudden chords of music.

Rachel Annard Taylor

Music Makers

Johann Sebastian Bach

The family name of Bach was well known to many music lovers two hundred years before Johann Sebastian Bach was born in Eisenach in 1685. Most of the Bachs made their living as musicians, but even those who were millers, bakers, or cabinet-makers could also make music.

Sebastian's father was an organist, a violinist, and a teacher. As soon as Sebastian was old enough he was taught music by his father. When he was eight years old he was singing in a choir.

Once a year all of the Bachs came together for a three-day festival. At these family reunions they had a lot of fun singing and playing music that they had composed themselves. Often they would make up two or more tunes to be sung or played at the same time. Sometimes they made up jolly songs, and at other times beautiful and majestic songs, like the music in a great cathedral.

When Sebastian was ten his father and mother died, and he went to live with an older brother who also was a church organist. Sebastian sang in the boys' choir in the church and he was taught to play the clavier, the piano of that day.

In the brother's library was a large book containing music of the masters. Sebastian begged to see this music, but his brother said, "Not until you are older." His longing for the book grew until, one cold night when everyone was asleep, he crept down the stairs and slipped the great book from the top shelf of a bookcase. Then he crept back to his room, which was flooded with moonlight, and began to copy the music, studying each page as he copied. He did this every moonlight night for six months. Now he had the music in his head and heart as well as in a book of his own. For several days he enjoyed playing this music, but then his brother saw the book and took it away from him. "All the beautiful music is gone," thought Sebastian; but when he sat down to the clavier he was overjoyed to find that the music was still in his mind and fingers.

There was a famous choir two hundred miles away. Sebastian and a friend decided to walk this long distance in order to try for places in the choir school. Imagine how happy they were when the choir master said, "Yes, I need both of you."

Sebastian was now allowed to study all the books in the library. He played the clavier for hours, and sometimes he played his violin in church. But the greatest thrill came when he was allowed to play the organ.

When he grew to be a man his fame as an organist spread far and wide. Soon he was playing the organ in Weimar, and he also wrote music for choirs and orchestras. He stayed in Weimar for nine years. By this time many courts begged for his services. Finally he decided to go to the big city of Leipzig, where he became the organist and director of the choir at the church of Saint Thomas.

Bach's wife was a gifted singer, and two of his twenty children became fine musicians. On many evenings the family gathered around their father and made beautiful music.

When Bach was older he became totally blind. However, he continued to compose music by telling one of his sons what to write down on the music paper. At his death he left to the world a large amount of great music that inspires musicians and music lovers even to this day.

My Heart Ever Faithful

From the "Pentecost Cantata"
Johann Sebastian Bach (Abridged)
Moderately fast, with rhythmic movement
so (5)
My heart · ev-er faith-ful, Sing prais - es, be joy - ful.
My heart · ev-er faith - ful, Sing prais - es, be joy - ful, Sing
prais - es, be joy - ful, Our Fa - ther is near. My
heart · ev-er faith - ful, Sing prais - es, be joy - ful, Sing
prais - es, be joy - ful, Our Fa - ther is here.

Jesu, Joy of Man's Desiring

Choral from Cantata No. 147
Johann Sebastian Bach

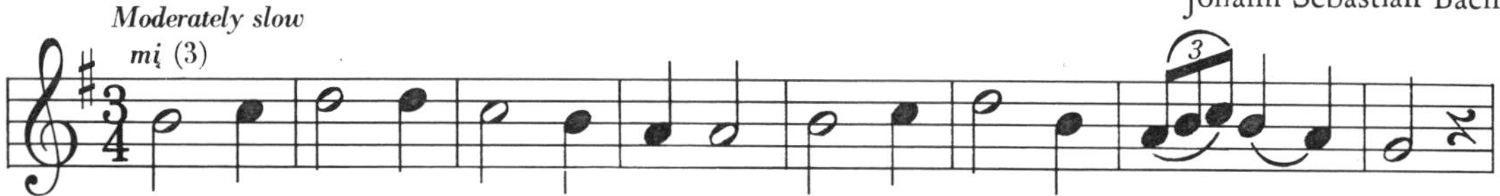
Moderately slow
mi (3)

1. Je - su, joy of man's de - sir - ing, Ho - ly wis-dom, love · most · bright,
2. Through the way where hope is guid-ing, Hark, what peace-ful mu - sic · rings!

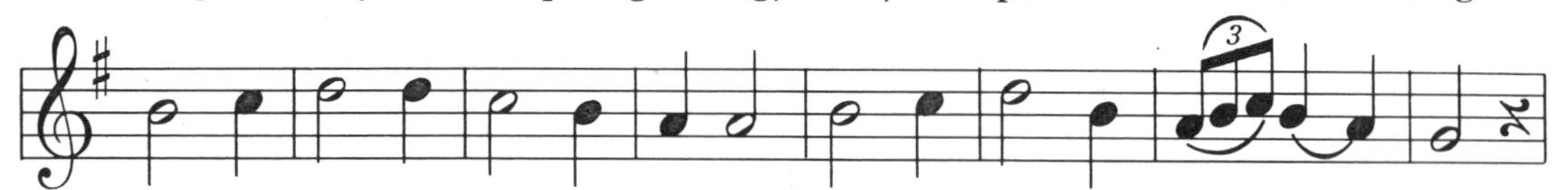

Drawn by Thee, our souls as - pir - ing Soar to un - cre - a - ted light.
Where the flocks in Thee con - fid - ing Drink of joy from death-less springs.

Word of God, our flesh that fash-ioned With the fire of life im - pas-sioned,
Theirs is beau-ty's fair - est pleas-ure, Theirs is wis-dom's ho - liest treas-ure.

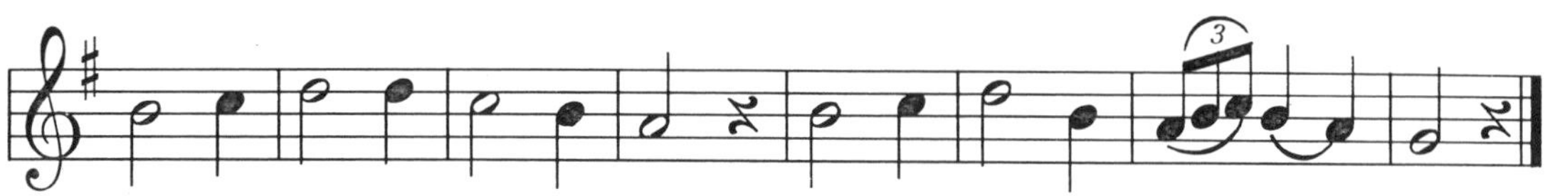

Striv - ing still to truth un - known, Soar-ing, sing - ing round·Thy · throne.
Thou dost ev - er lead Thine own, In the love of joy · un - known.

Listen to "Jesu, Joy of Man's Desiring" (Chorale-Prelude), Bach. (Victor or Columbia record.)

Jesu, Joy of Man's Desiring

Adapted and arranged for string quartet, three violins and cello, by L. E. Watters

First violin.
Second violin.
Third violin.
Cello.

Minuet in G Major

Rather quick and graceful

Johann Sebastian Bach

Very often the "Minuet in G Minor" is played right after the "Minuet in G Major," as though they were one selection.

Minuet in G Minor

Rather quick and graceful
Johann Sebastian Bach

"No music for my son," said Dr. Handel. "He is to be a lawyer." But when George was six and went to school, the brightest moments of the day for him were when the music master came and played on a small spinet. "I wish I might have a spinet," George would often say. But Dr. Handel would repeat, "You are going to be a lawyer."

On the morning of his seventh birthday George was wakened by his Aunt Anna. What did she have with her? He sprang out of bed. "Aunt Anna, a spinet for me?" "Quiet, my dear; you must not play it here. We will take it to the attic, where you can play without annoying anyone." After that George spent many happy hours at his spinet in the attic.

One day Dr. Handel was called to the royal court of the Duke of Wessenfels, forty miles from the Handel home in Halle. George had heard about the beautiful music at the court and he begged to go along. "Not this time, my son"; and Dr. Handel rode away in his horse-drawn coach.

George watched sorrowfully for a while, and then started to run after the coach as fast as he could go. It was almost noonday when the horses stopped to rest. Dr. Handel heard a voice. He looked down the road and saw his little son begging to be taken along. George was too tired to be sent back, so the father took him into the coach, and the dust-covered, weary boy leaned against him and slept. When evening came they arrived at Wessenfels.

In the days that followed, while the doctor was busy George listened to the organ in the chapel. What beautiful music! He crept closer and closer, until the organist made room for him on the bench. Then George played some of the little pieces he had learned on his spinet. The organist was astonished at his skill, and every day after that George was given a chance to play the organ.

When Sunday came he was again sitting beside the organist. Imagine his surprise when his new friend said, "George, you play until the end of the service."

After the service the Duke said, "That little boy playing such difficult music without a mistake! Send his father to me." The Duke insisted that Dr. Handel allow the boy to study with the greatest musician in Halle.

In those happy days George not only studied organ, but he also learned to write down the music that sang in his heart and mind. He also learned to play the violin and oboe. When he was seventeen he was made organist of the cathedral.

A few years later young Handel became the director of the opera in Hamburg. Here he wrote his first opera. But Italy was the center of opera, and Handel was delighted to accept an invitation to visit that country. There his experiences and friendships were wonderful. However, when the Prince of Hanover came to Italy and invited Handel to take charge of the music at his court he accepted at once.

Handel liked to travel, and before long he wanted to visit England. When the

Prince reluctantly gave his consent he added, "But come back soon."

London—how wonderful! Soon Handel was writing music for the opera and the cathedral, and at the request of Queen Anne he wrote music for a great celebration. He was so busy and so happy that he kept putting off his return to Hanover.

Soon Queen Anne died, and the Prince of Hanover, who was next in line, came to England and was crowned George I, King of England. When Handel heard this he thought, "Will the King be angry because I stayed away from Hanover so long? What shall I do?" Handel thought and thought. When he heard that a boating party was to be given on the River Thames in honor of the new king he said, "That's it. I'll write some special music for the party." So Handel composed a group of pieces to be played by an orchestra. When the King heard this beautiful "Water Music" he was much pleased. He not only forgave Handel, but he also granted him two hundred pounds for every year that he stayed in England and served the King with his music.

Toward the end of his life Handel wrote the wonderful oratorio "Messiah." The melodies came crowding into his mind so fast that he wrote the whole oratorio in twenty-four days. When it was given in England the majesty of the Hallelujah Chorus so impressed the King that he rose to his feet; and since that day all people stand when the Hallelujah Chorus is sung.

Drawing based on Dicksee "The Child Handel," copyright Art Education, Inc., N. Y.

He Shall Feed His Flock

From "The Messiah"
George Frederick Handel
Tenderly
so (5)
He · shall feed His flock like a shep - herd, And
He · shall gath - er the lambs with His arm, with · · His arm.
He · shall feed His flock like a shep - herd, And
He · shall · gath - er the lambs with His arm, with · · His arm.
And car - ry · them · in His bos - om, And
gen - tly lead · those · · that are · · with young, · And
gen-tly lead those, And gen - tly lead · those that are · with young.

Listen to "The Pastoral Symphony," from *The Messiah,* Handel. (Victor record.)

Largo from "Xerxes"

George Frederick Handel
Arranged by L. E. Watters

Broadly
3

Listen to "Largo," from *Xerxes*, Handel. (Victor or Columbia record.)

Melody from the Opera "Rinaldo"

Violin
Smoothly - not too fast
George Frederick Handel
Adapted and arranged by L. E. Watters
Piano
Fine
D.C. al Fine

Listen to "Leave Me to Languish," from *Rinaldo,* Handel. (Victor Listening Album Six.)

Halloween

I saw three witches
That bowed down like barley,
And straddled their brooms 'neath a louring sky,
And, mounting a storm-cloud,
Aloft on its margin,
Stood black in the silver as up they did fly.

Walter de la Mare

Halloween Visitor

Frances Ford — Nadine Bensley

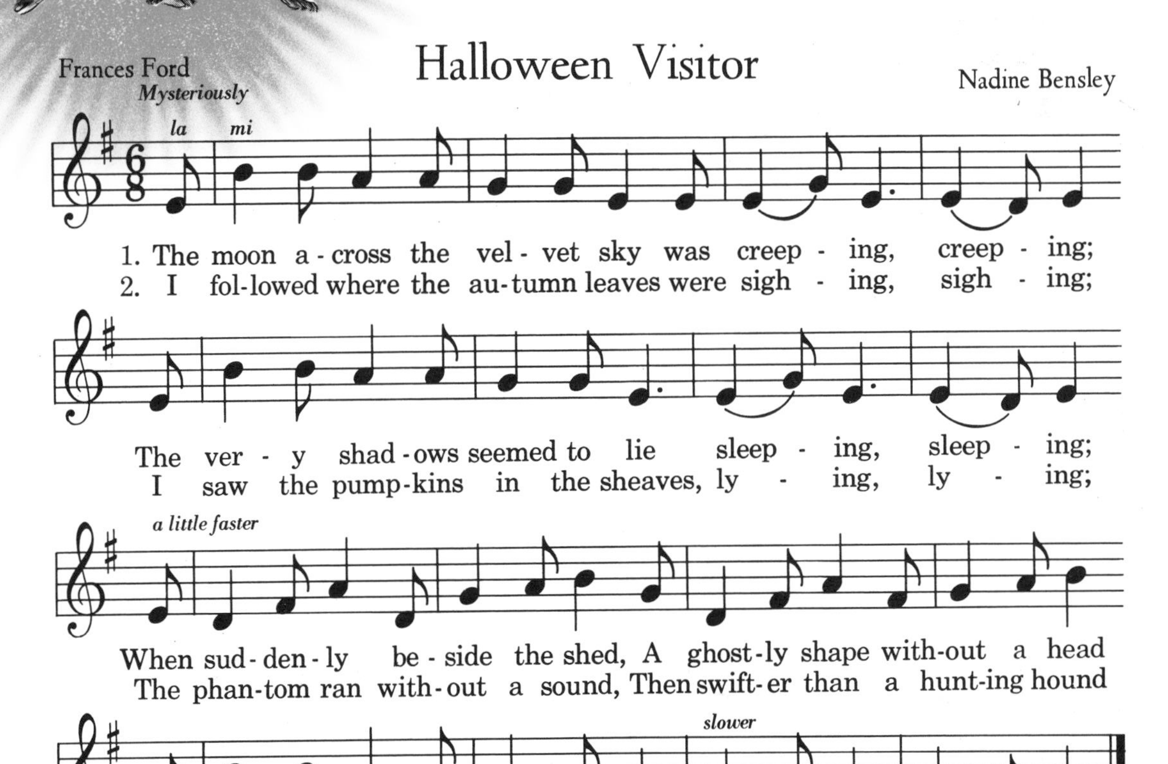
Mysteriously
la mi
1. The moon a - cross the vel - vet sky was creep - ing, creep - ing;
2. I fol-lowed where the au-tumn leaves were sigh - ing, sigh - ing;
The ver - y shad - ows seemed to lie sleep - ing, sleep - ing;
I saw the pump-kins in the sheaves, ly - ing, ly - ing;
a little faster
When sud - den - ly be - side the shed, A ghost-ly shape with-out a head
The phan-tom ran with-out a sound, Then swift-er than a hunt-ing hound
slower

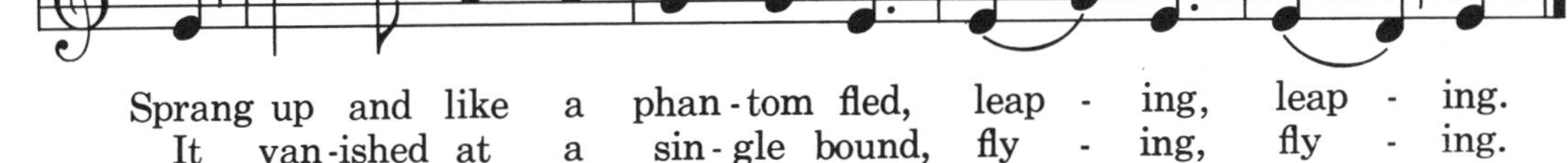
Sprang up and like a phan - tom fled, leap - ing, leap - ing.
It van-ished at a sin - gle bound, fly - ing, fly - ing.

Listen to "Danse Macabre," Saint-Saëns. (Decca, Victor or Columbia record.)
Listen to "Witches' Dance," MacDowell. (Victor Listening Album Five.)

Thanksgiving
As once our Pilgrim Fathers knelt
And offered thanks beneath the sky
With American hearts for American earth,
Let us be thankful, you and I.
Frances Frost
Now Thank We All Our God
Martin Rinkart, 1636
Translated by Catherine Winkworth
Johann Crüger, 1647
With majesty
so (5)
1. Now thank we all our God With heart and hands and voic - es, Who
2. O may this boun-teous God Through all our life be near us, With
won-drous things hath done, In Whom His world re - joic - es; Who
ev - er joy - ful hearts And bless - ed peace to cheer us; And
fi (♮4)
from our moth - ers' arms Hath blessed us on our way With
keep us in His grace, And guide · us when per - plexed, And
count - less gifts of love, And still is ours to - day.
free us from all ills In this world and the next.

Prayer of Thanksgiving

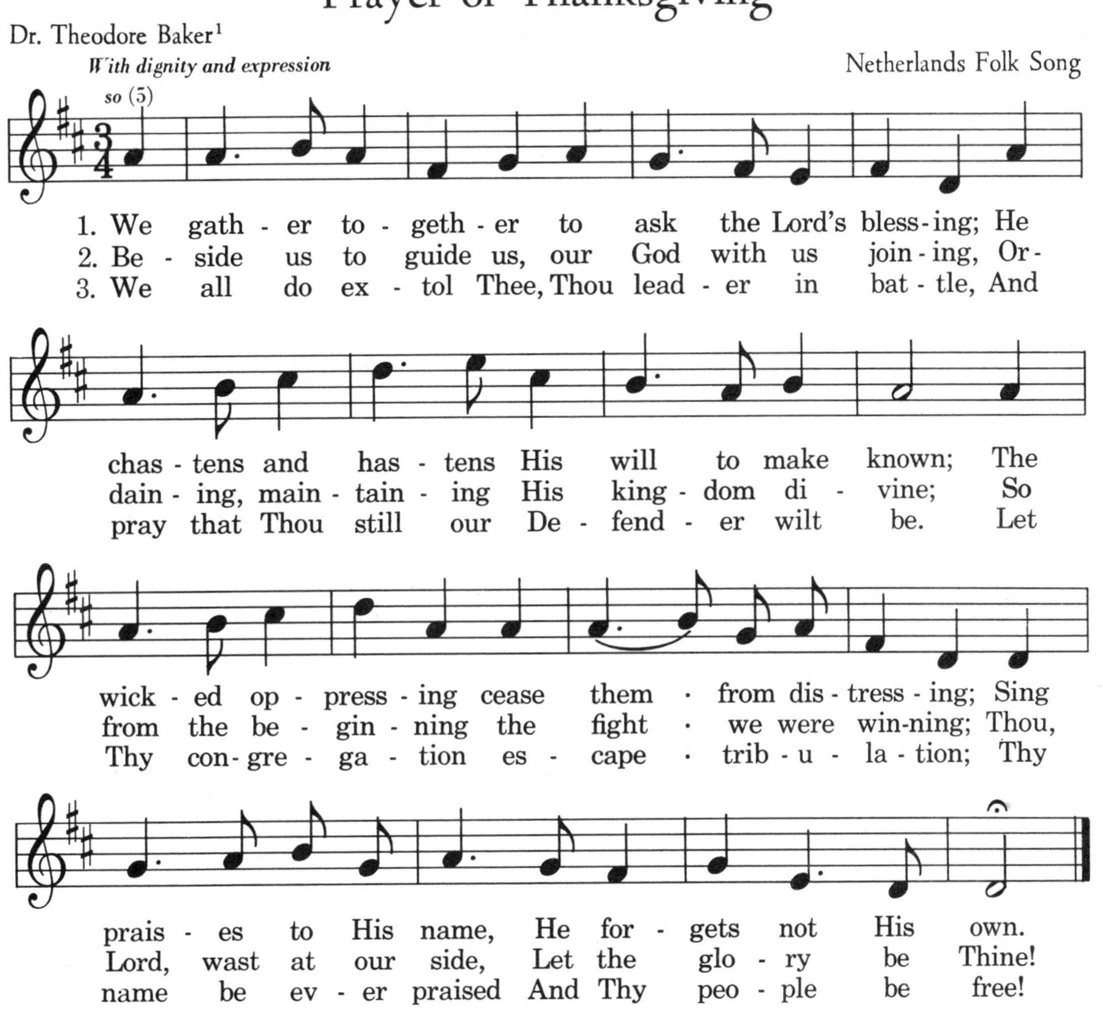
Dr. Theodore Baker[1]
With dignity and expression
Netherlands Folk Song
so (5)
1. We gath - er to - geth - er to ask the Lord's bless - ing; He
2. Be - side us to guide us, our God with us join - ing, Or -
3. We all do ex - tol Thee, Thou lead - er in bat - tle, And
chas - tens and has - tens His will to make known; The
dain - ing, main - tain - ing His king - dom di - vine; So
pray that Thou still our De - fend - er wilt be. Let
wick - ed op - press - ing cease them from dis - tress - ing; Sing
from the be - gin - ning the fight we were win - ning; Thou,
Thy con - gre - ga - tion es - cape trib - u - la - tion; Thy
prais - es to His name, He for - gets not His own.
Lord, wast at our side, Let the glo - ry be Thine!
name be ev - er praised And Thy peo - ple be free!

[1]English version copyright, 1894, by G. Schirmer, Inc. Copyright renewal assigned, 1923, to G. Schirmer, Inc. Printed by permission.

Come, Ye Thankful People, Come

Henry Alford

George J. Elvey

With processional rhythm

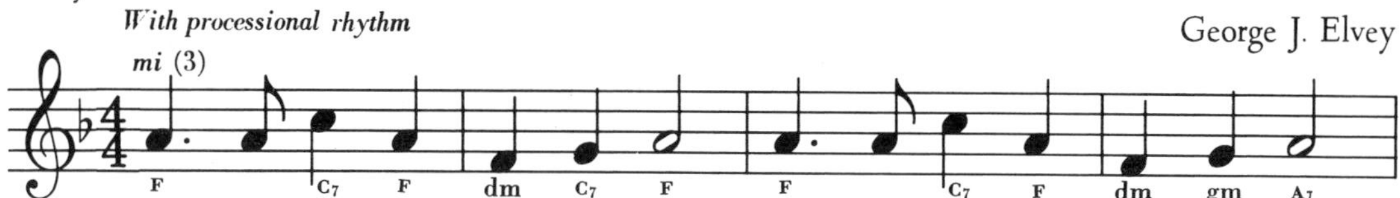
mi (3)
F C7 F dm C7 F F C7 F dm gm A7

1. Come, ye thank-ful peo - ple, come, Raise the song of har - vest home;
2. All the world is God's own field, Fruit un - to His praise to yield;

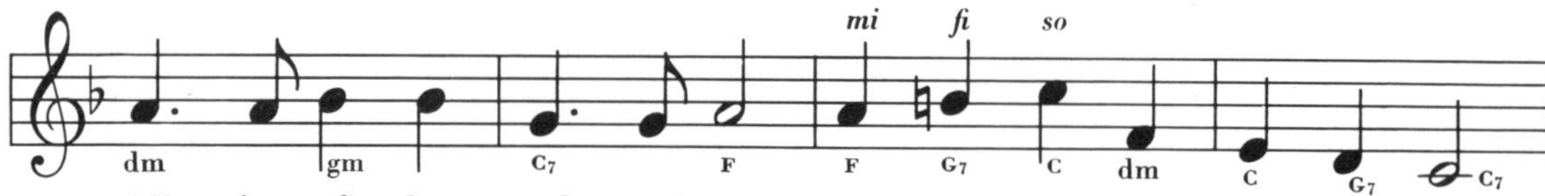
mi fi so
dm gm C7 F F G7 C dm C G7 C7

All is safe - ly gath - ered in, Ere the win - ter storms be - gin;
Wheat and tares there - in are sown, Un - to joy or sor - row grown;

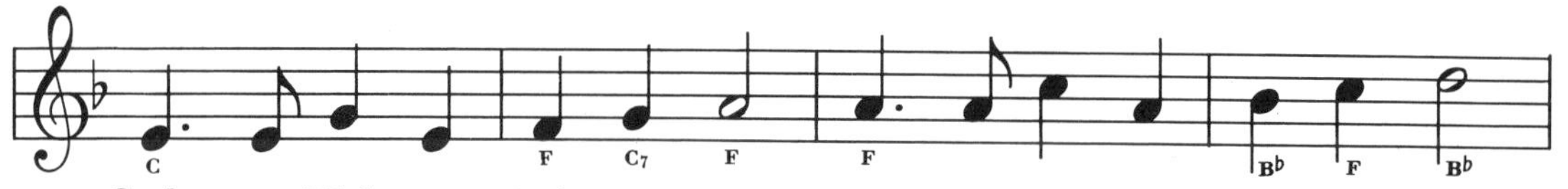
C F C7 F F B♭ F B♭

God, our Mak - er, doth pro - vide For our wants to be sup - plied;
Rip - 'ning with a won-drous pow'r Till the fin - al Har-vest hour.

D7 gm C7 F B♭ F F C7 F

Come to God's own tem - ple, come, Raise the song of har - vest home.
Grant, O Lord of life, that we Ho - ly grain and pure may be.

Orchestration for Come, Ye Thankful People, Come

Violins, flutes, and bells.

Arranged by L. E. Watters

B flat Clarinets, B flat cornets and trumpets.
E flat Altos and E flat saxophones.
Cellos, trombones and baritones.
Drums.
roll

Christmas

God bless your house this holy night,
And all within it;

God bless the candle that you light
To midnight's minute.

Eleanor Farjeon[1]

Christmas Bells

1.
mi (3)
2.
Big Ben Chimes
Big bells do chime, Christ - mas is here;
To thee and thine, Peace and good cheer.

Pray God Bless

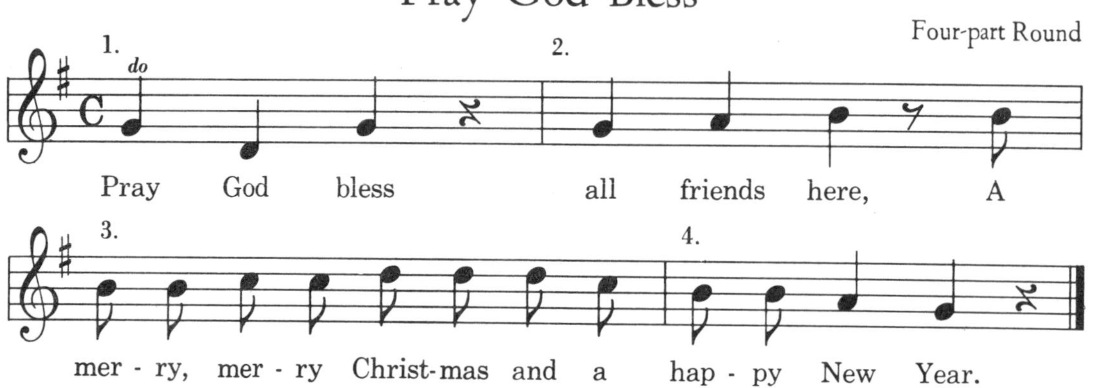

1.
do
2.
Four-part Round
Pray God bless all friends here, A
3.
4.
mer - ry, mer - ry Christ-mas and a hap - py New Year.

[1]From *Sing for Your Supper,* copyright 1938 by Eleanor Farjeon. Reprinted by permission of J. B. Lippincott Company.

Joseph Mohr
Silent Night
Smoothly, not too slow
5 (so)
3 (mi)
Franz Gruber
C C G7 C
1. Si - lent night! Ho - ly night! All is calm, all is bright
2. Si - lent night! Ho - ly night! Shep - herds quake at the sight,
3. Si - lent night! Ho - ly night! Son of God, love's pure light
F C F C
Round yon Vir - gin Moth-er and Child! Ho - ly In-fant, so ten-der and mild,
Glo - ries stream from heav-en a - far, Heav'n-ly hosts · sing Al - le-lu - ia;
Ra-diant beams from Thy ho - ly face, With the dawn of re - deem - ing grace,
G7 C C G7 C
Sleep in heav-en-ly peace, · Sleep · in heav-en-ly peace. ·
Christ, the Sav-iour, is born! · Christ, the Sav-iour, is born! ·
Je - sus, Lord, at Thy birth! · Je - sus, Lord, at Thy birth! ·

One of you play this on the piano while the others sing.

O Little Town of Bethlehem

Phillips Brooks

Lewis H. Redner

Sweetly
3(*mi*)
♯2 (*ri*)

1. O lit - tle town of Beth - le - hem, How still we · see thee lie,
2. For Christ is born of Ma - ry, And gath - ered · all a - bove,

A - bove thy deep and dream-less sleep The si - lent · stars go by;
While mor - tals sleep, the an - gels keep Their watch of · won-d'ring love.

Yet in thy dark streets shin - eth The ev - er - last - ing light,
O morn - ing stars, to - geth - er Pro - claim the ho - ly birth,

The hopes and fears of all the years Are met in thee to - night.
And prais - es sing to God the King, And peace to men on earth.

Shepherds and the Star

Translated by Marchette Gaylord Chute

Syrian Folk Song

Smoothly
la

1. All the fields their si - lence keep, All the lambs are fast a - sleep;
2. Once these fields were bright as day, So the old - er shep-herds say,
3. It was filled with forms of light, Love - ly forms, whose wings were bright.
4. Next time an - gels come this way I shall hear the things they say;

Listen to "Shepherds' Christmas Music," from *Christmas Oratorio*, Bach.. (Victor record.)

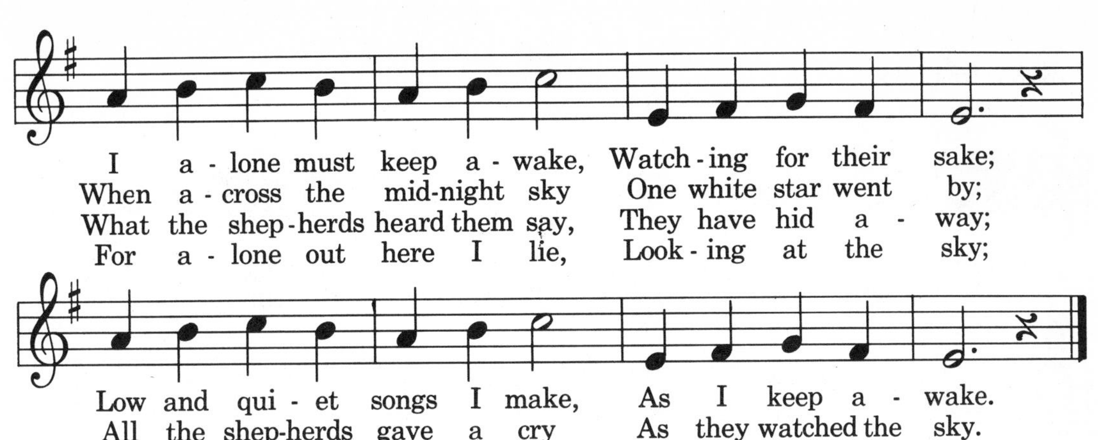
I a - lone must keep a - wake, Watch - ing for their sake;
When a - cross the mid-night sky One white star went by;
What the shep - herds heard them say, They have hid a - way;
For a - lone out here I lie, Look - ing at the sky;
Low and qui - et songs I make, As I keep a - wake.
All the shep-herds gave a cry As they watched the sky.
I can nev - er make them say What they heard that day.
We shall see that star go by, Lit - tle lambs and I.

English version
by Christine Turner Curtis

Christmas Lullaby

Polish Folk Song

Gently
3 (mi)
1 (do)
1. Loo - lull - a - by, Je - su,[1] and safe be Thy sleep - ing;
2. Loo - lull - a - by, Je - su, our car - ols we sing Thee;
Near Thee is Thy Moth - er, Her still vig - il keep - ing.
Loaves made of fine wheat and ripe ber - ries we bring Thee.
Thou art like a star ev - er - more the heav - ens a - dorn - ing.
Down come snow - y an - gels Thy ho - ly cra - dle at - tend - ing,
Thou art the white rose - bud that o - pens at morn - ing.
Loo - lull - a - by, Je - su, till night - time is end - ing.

[1] *Pronounce* yā′so͞o.

Carol of the Grasses

Katherine Smith Bolt

Moderately la (6)

Powell Weaver

1. Nev-er be-fore was grass so green As in that mead-ow long · · a - go, ·
2. Nev-er so gold be-fore, they said, The har-vest of the win - ter hay. ·

The gen-tle songs of sum-mer rain · sang low, · sang low.
The plum-éd heads bent low as if · to pray, as if to pray.

3. Nev-er was man-ger mound so soft: The grass curves gen-tly 'neath His head. ·

The lit - tle Je - sus sleeps · with - in · this bed. · ·

O Mary[1]

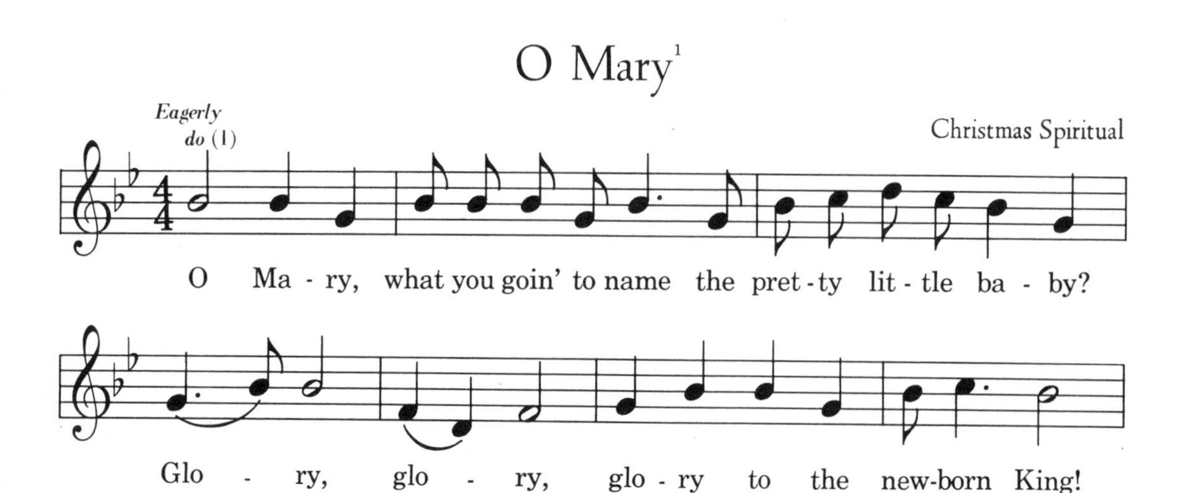
Eagerly
do (1)
Christmas Spiritual
O Ma - ry, what you goin' to name the pret - ty lit - tle ba - by?
Glo - ry, glo - ry, glo - ry to the new-born King!

[1]From the book *American Negro Songs*, copyrighted 1940 by John W. Work. Assigned to Theodore Presser Company in 1948. Used by permission.

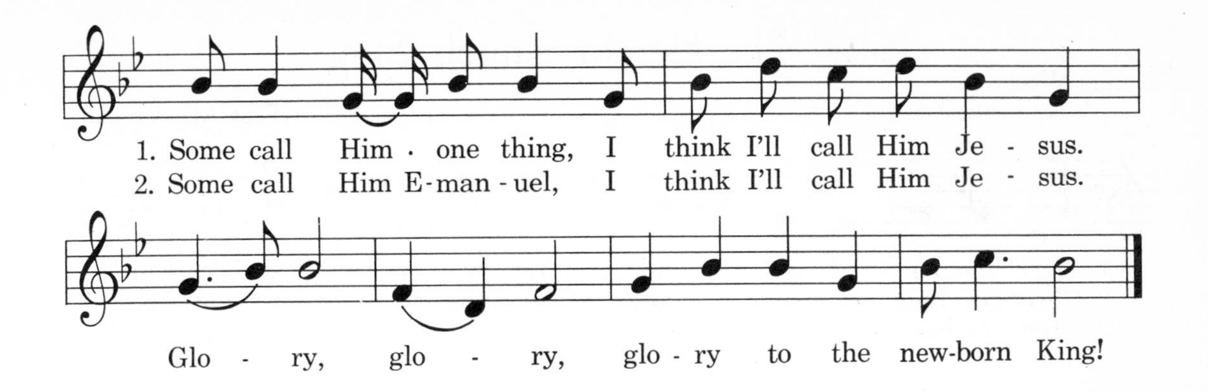
1. Some call Him · one thing, I think I'll call Him Je - sus.
2. Some call Him E-man-uel, I think I'll call Him Je - sus.
Glo - ry, glo - ry, glo - ry to the new-born King!

Lullaby on Christmas Eve

Albert J. Lange (Norwegian)
Translated by Oscar R. Overby

Moderately and gently F. Melius Christiansen

3 (*mi*)
1. Moth-er her vig - il is keep - ing, Hush, lit-tle babe, to her song; ·
2. Moth-er in fer-vent de - vo - tion Bends o'er thy cra-dle to - night, ·
3. Babe of my bos-om, be wing-ing Soft-ly where dream-lands be-gin; ·

Rest thee se-cure in thy sleep - ing, Grow thee more state-ly and strong.
Shields from all earth-ly com-mo - tion, Shel-ters her treas-ured de-light, ·
Christ-mas Eve bells are a - ring - ing, Fes-tive-ly call-ing thee in. ·

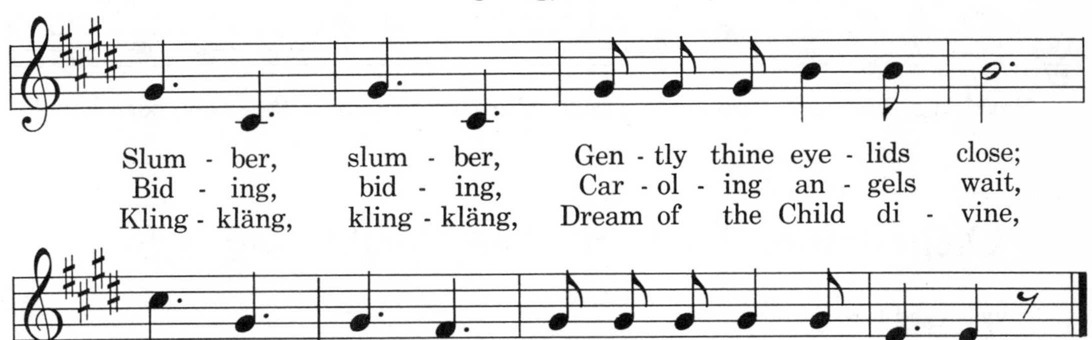
Slum - ber, slum - ber, Gen - tly thine eye - lids close;
Bid - ing, bid - ing, Car - ol - ing an - gels wait,
Kling - kläng, kling - kläng, Dream of the Child di - vine,
Slum - ber, slum - ber, Cra-dled in sweet re - pose. ·
Bid - ing, bid - ing, Vig - il at heav - en's gate. ·
Kling - kläng, kling-kläng, Dear lit - tle babe of mine. ·

Hark! The Herald Angels Sing

Charles Wesley
In processional rhythm
so (5) do (1)
Felix Mendelssohn
1. Hark! the her - ald an - gels sing, · "Glo - ry to the new born King!
2. Christ, by high - est heav'n a - dored; Christ, the ev - er - last - ing Lord;
3. Hail! the heav'n-born Prince of Peace! Hail! the Sun of Right-eous-ness!
Peace on earth, and mer - cy mild, · God and sin - ners re - con - ciled."
Late in time be - hold Him come, · Off - spring of the fa - vored one.
Light and life to all He brings, Ris'n with heal - ing in His wings.
Joy - ful, all ye na - tions, rise, · Join the tri - umph of the skies; ·
Veiled in flesh, the God-head see; · Hail th'in - car - nate De - i - ty, ·
Mild He lays His glo - ry by, · Born that man no more may die: ·
With th'an - gel - ic host pro - claim, "Christ is · born in Beth - le - hem."
Pleased as man with men to dwell, Je - sus, our Im - man - u - el!
Born to raise the sons of earth, Born to · give them sec - ond birth.
Hark! the her - ald an - gels sing, "Glo - ry · to the new - born King!"

Orchestration for Hark! The Herald Angels Sing

Violins and flutes play voice part.

Arranged by L. E. Watters

B flat Clarinets, B flat cornets and trumpets.

(B flat Clarinets, B flat cornets and trumpets continued.)
E flat Altos and E flat saxophones.
Cellos, trombones and baritones.

The Wondrous Child
Translated by Susanna Myers
Happily
5 (so)
French Carol
1. Come, shep - herds, come! Now leave the vil - lage, hast'n - ing.
2. There you will find Him Ly - ing in a sta - ble,
Lay down your crooks Be - side your sleep - ing flocks;
A Child so fair, So lit - tle, gen - tle, dear;
Be sad no more, But join in great re - joic - ing.
Give Him your love, Whose love di - vine is a - ble
Come quick - ly to a - dore The Child, the Child,
To give us heav - en's peace; A - dore the Child,
The won - drous Child of Christ - mas morn.
The won - drous Child of Christ - mas morn.
120

The Angels in Our Fields
Translated by Cecil Cowdrey
Moderately, with motion
mi (3)
French Carol
(All) 1. High a - bove our · mead - ows wing - ing,
(Shepherds) 2. Tell us, an - gels, · to whose glo - ry
(Angels) 3. Shep - herds, in a · sta - ble low - ly,
(Shepherds) 4. Let us seek the · vil - lage yon - der,
An - gels in - tone their · heav'n - ly strain; Far from lis - t'ning ·
Sound ye this chant from · star - ry skies. Say what king, what ·
Soft - ly the Christ-child · sleeps to - night. Cra - dled all in ·
There will we kneel the · Babe be - fore. Lov - ing hom - age ·
moun - tains ring - ing, Ech - o re - peats the · glad re - frain.
proph - et hoar - y Mer - its these glad tri - um - phant cries?
ra - diance ho - ly Li - eth the King of · love and light.
we will ren - der, Hum - bly with won - d'ring hearts a - dore.
Glo - - - - - - - ri - a in ex - cel - sis De - o,
Glo - - - - - - - ri - a in ex - cel - sis De - o.
G E7 am D7 G am D7 G D7 G C G D7
121

On a Winter Morning

Translated by Susanna Myers

Brightly

French Carol

mi re do so do la so

1. Once to Beth-l'hem shep-herds came On a win-ter morn-ing,
2. So we make our gifts to-day, On a win-ter morn-ing,

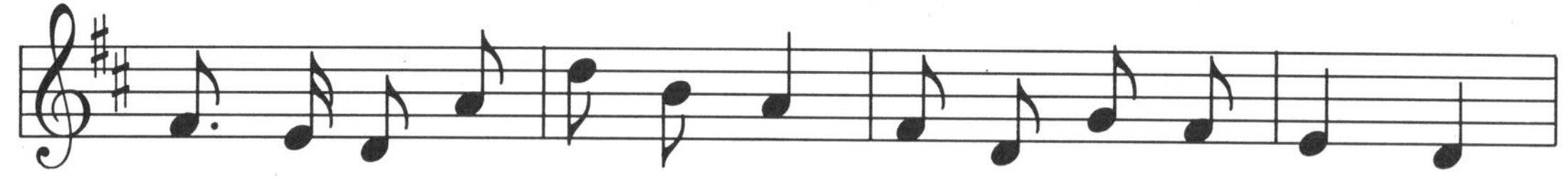

There to kneel be-fore the Child As the day was dawn-ing.
Think-ing of the Christ Child dear Born on Christ-mas morn-ing.

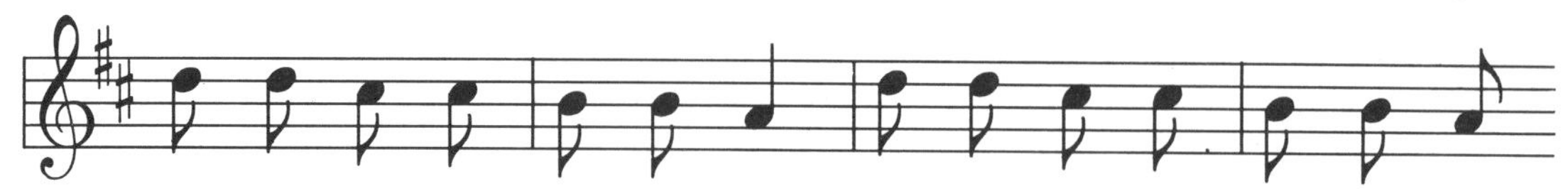

One had brought a lit-tle lamb, One, a wool-ly sheep-skin warm,
For the ones we love the best, And for those who have the least,

With · love they came, their · gifts to bring,
In · love we give our · gifts to-day,

For the Child who was born in Beth-l'hem On that win-ter morn-ing.
In · love for the Child of Beth-l'hem, Born on Christ-mas morn-ing.

Twelve Days of Christmas

English Folk Song

Gaily
so (5)
fa (4)

1. The first day of Christ-mas my true love sent to me A

par - te-ridge in a pear tree. 2. The sec-ond day of Christ-mas my

true love sent to me Two tur-tle doves and a par - te-ridge in a pear

tree. 3. The third day of Christ-mas my true love sent to me Three French hens,
4. The fourth day of Christ-mas my true love sent to me Four call-ing birds,

two tur - tle doves and a par - te-ridge in a pear tree.

Repeat measure for stanzas 4 to 12 as often as necessary, singing the starred text in reverse order, ending each stanza with "two turtle doves and a parteridge in a pear tree."*

5. The fifth day . . . . . *Five golden rings,
6. The sixth day . . . . *Six geese a-laying,
7. The seventh day . . *Seven swans a-swimming,
8. The eighth day . . . *Eight maids a-milking,
9. The ninth day . . . . *Nine fiddlers fiddling,
10. The tenth day . . . . *Ten drummers drumming,
11. The eleventh day . . *Eleven ladies dancing,
12. The twelfth day . . . *Twelve lords a-leaping,

Patriotic Days

Tossed by the wind against the blue sky,
The flag of our country
Waves gently on high.

Long, long ago when our country was new,
Men thought up this flag
Of red, white and blue.

They thought of the stripes and the field of blue,
With the white pointed stars
Shining brightly through.

They gave us this flag, and everyone knows
It stands for our country
Wherever it blows.

The Star-Spangled Banner

Francis Scott Key — John Stafford Smith

so (5)
1. Oh, · say! can you see, · by the dawn's ear - ly light,
2. On the shore, dim - ly seen · through the mists of the deep,
3. Oh, · thus be it ev - er when · free - men shall stand
What so proud - ly we hailed at the twi - light's last gleam - ing,
Where the foe's haugh - ty host in dread si - lence re - pos - es,
Be - tween their loved homes and the war's des - o - la - tion!
Whose broad stripes and bright stars, through the per - il - ous fight,
What is that which the breeze, o'er the tow - er - ing steep,
Blest with vic - t'ry and peace, may the heav'n - res - cued land

O'er the ram - parts we watched were so gal - lant - ly stream - ing?
As it fit - ful - ly blows, half con - ceals, half dis - clos - es?
Praise the Pow'r that hath made and pre - served us a na - tion!

And the rock - ets' red glare, the bombs burst - ing in air,
Now it catch - es the gleam of the morn - ing's first beam,
Then · con - quer we must, when our cause it is just,

Gave · proof through the night · that our flag was still there.
In full glo - ry re - flect - ed now · shines on the stream;
And · this be our mot - to: "In · God is our trust!"

Oh, · say does that · Star - Span - gled Ban - ner · yet · wave ·
'Tis the Star-Span - gled · Ban - ner, oh, long may · it · wave ·
And the Star-Span - gled · Ban - ner in tri - umph · shall · wave ·

O'er the land · of the free and the home of the brave?
O'er the land · of the free and the home of the brave!
O'er the land · of the free and the home of the brave!

A mighty brain, a will to endure,
Passions subdued, a slave to none,
A heart that was brave and strong and sure,
A soul that was noble and great and pure,
A faith in God that was held secure—
This was George Washington.

Anonymous

A bronzed, lank man! His suit of ancient black,
A famous high top hat and plain, worn shawl
Make him the quaint great figure that men love,
The prairie lawyer, master of us all.

Vachel Lindsay

America

Samuel Francis Smith

Traditional

1 (do)

1. My coun-try, 'tis of thee, Sweet land of lib - er - ty, Of thee I sing.
2. My na - tive coun-try, thee, Land of the no - ble free, Thy name I love.
3. Our fa-thers' God! to Thee, Au-thor of lib - er - ty, To Thee we sing.

Land where my fa - thers died! Land of the Pil - grims' pride!
I love thy rocks and rills, Thy woods and tem - pled hills;
Long may our land be bright With free - dom's ho - ly light;

From ev - 'ry · moun - tain - side, Let · free - dom ring!
My heart · with · rap - ture thrills Like · that a - bove.
Pro - tect · us · by Thy might, Great · God our King!

Orchestration for America

Violins and flutes play the voice parts.
Arranged by L. E. Watters
B flat Clarinets, B flat saxophones, B flat cornets and trumpets.
E flat Altos (mellophones) and E flat saxophones.
Cellos, trombones and baritones.

Dixie

Dan D. Emmett

Dan D. Emmett

Quickly
5 (so)

1. I · wish I was · in the land of cot - ton, Old times there · are
2. There buck-wheat cakes and · In - dian bat - ter Make you fat or a

not for - got-ten, Look a - way! Look a - way! Look a - way! Dix - ie
lit - tle fat-ter, Look a - way! Look a - way! Look a - way! Dix - ie

Land! In · Dix - ie Land where I was born · Ear - ly on one
Land! Then hoe it down and scratch your grav-el, to Dix-ie's Land I'm

frost - y morn, Look a - way! Look a - way! Look a - way! Dix - ie Land!
bound to trav-el, Look a - way! Look a - way! Look a - way! Dix - ie Land!

Chorus

Then I wish I was in Dix - ie, Hoo - ray! (hoo-ray) Hoo-ray! (hoo-ray)
do. . . . . fa . . . . re. . . . . so. . . . .

In Dix - ie Land I'll take my stand To live and die in Dix - ie,
do . . . . fa . . . . do . . . . so. . . . .

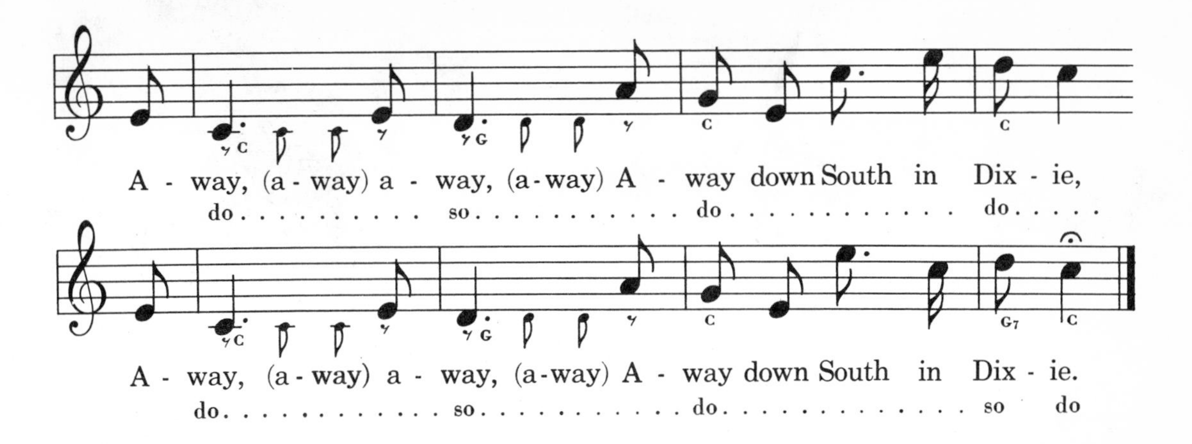
C G C C
A - way, (a - way) a - way, (a-way) A - way down South in Dix - ie,
do . . . . so . . . . do . . . . do . . . . .
C G C G7 C
A - way, (a - way) a - way, (a-way) A - way down South in Dix - ie.
do . . . . so . . . . do . . . . so do

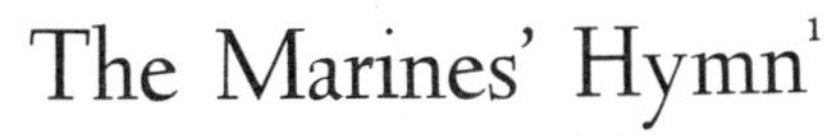

The Marines' Hymn[1]

In march time

do (1)

1. From the Halls of Mon - te - zu - ma To the shores of Trip - o - li;
2. Our flag's un-furl'd to ev -'ry breeze From dawn to set-ting sun;
3. Here's health to you and to our Corps Which we are proud to serve;

We fight our coun-try's bat - tles In the air, on land and sea;
We have fought in ev -'ry clime and place Where we could take a gun;
In many a strife we've fought for life And nev - er lost our nerve;

First to fight for right and free - dom And to keep our hon-or clean;
In the snow of far off North-ern lands And in sun-ny trop - ic scenes,
If the Ar - my and the Na - vy Ev-er look on Heav-en's scenes,

We are proud to claim the ti - tle Of U - nit - ed States Ma - rines.
You will find us al - ways on the job, The U - nit - ed States Ma - rines.
They will find the streets are guard - ed By U - nit - ed States Ma - rines.

O Canada!

R. Stanley Weir

C. Lavallee

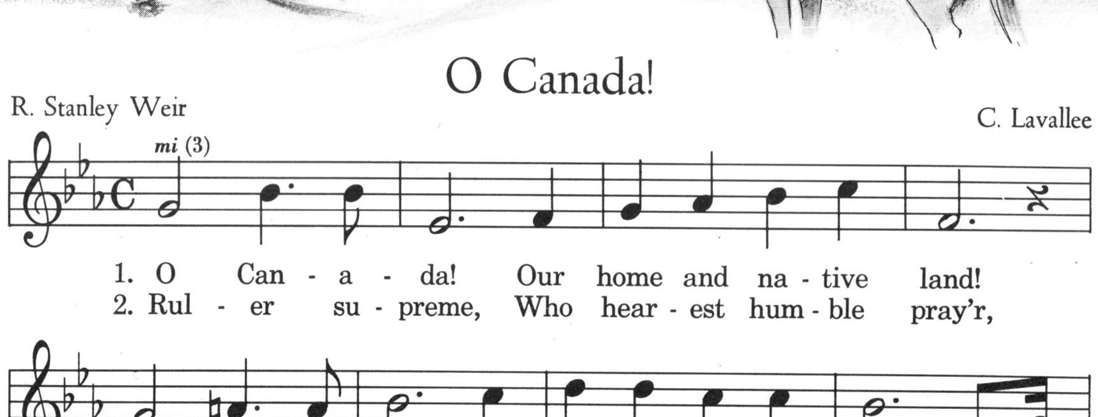
mi (3)

1. O Can - a - da! Our home and na - tive land!
2. Rul - er su - preme, Who hear - est hum - ble pray'r,

True pa - triot - love in all thy sons com - mand. With ·
Hold our Do - min - ion in Thy lov - ing care. Help ·

glow-ing hearts we · see thee rise, The True North strong and free; And ·
us to find, O · God, in Thee A · last - ing rich re - ward, As ·

stand on guard, O · Can - a - da, We stand on guard · for · thee.
wait - ing for the · bet - ter day, We ev - er stand · on · guard.

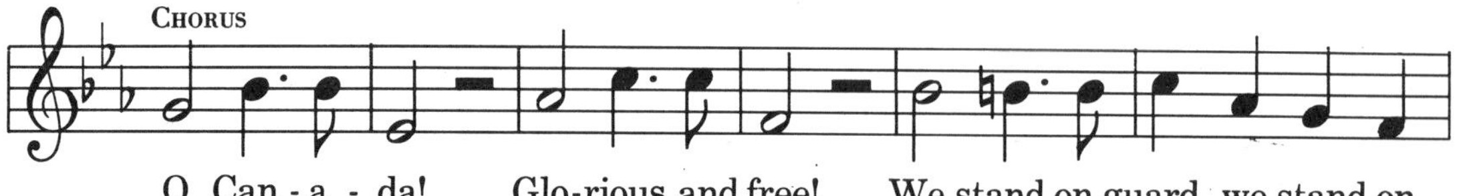
CHORUS

O Can - a - da! Glo-rious and free! We stand on guard, we stand on

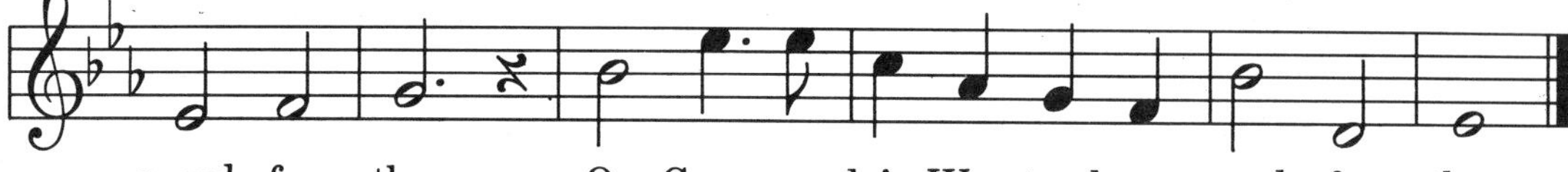

guard for thee. O Can - a - da! We stand on guard for thee.

Easter

A New Created World

Franz Joseph Haydn
Adapted and arranged by L. E. Watters

With spirit
A
B
C
A new cre - a - ted world, a · new cre - a - ted world Springs up, springs up at · God's com - mand.
A new cre - a - ted world, a · new cre - a - ted world Springs up, springs up at · God's com - mand, springs up at God's com - mand, springs up at God's com - mand.

Orchestration for "A New Created World"

Adapted and arranged by L. E. Watters

Violins
A
B
f
p

(Violins continued.)
C
f
p
f
A
Cellos
p
B
f
p
C
f
p
f
A
Flute
or
Bells
f
p
B
f
C
f
p
f

B flat Clarinets
A
B
C
B flat Cornets and Trumpets
7
E flat Altos and E flat Saxophones

Continued on next page.

(E flat Altos and E flat Saxophones continued.)
C
p
f
Trombone and Baritone
A
7
f
B
p
C
Drums
A
p
B
C
(roll)

THE WONDERFUL WORLD OUTSIDE

Watch honey-bees busy around the hive of a summer forenoon,
Or animals feeding in the fields,
Or birds, or the wonderfulness of insects in the air,
Or the wonderfulness of the sundown, or of the stars shining so quiet and bright,
Or the exquisite delicate thin curve of the new moon in spring;
These, one and all, are to me miracles.

Walt Whitman

Morning and Evening

A Summer Morning
Rachel Field
L. E. Watters
With expression
do (1)
I saw dawn creep a-cross the sky, And all the gulls go fly - ing by.
I saw the sea put on its dress Of blue mid-sum-mer love - li - ness,
And heard the trees · be-gin to stir Green arms of pine and ju - ni - per.
I heard the wind call out and say: "Get up, my dear, it is to-day!"

Listen to "Morning," from *Overture to William Tell*, Rossini.
Listen to "Morning," from *Peer Gynt Suite*, Grieg.

Morning Is Come

Round
1.
do (1)
2.
Morn - ing is come, Night is a - way;
Rise with the sun, · · And · wel - come the day.

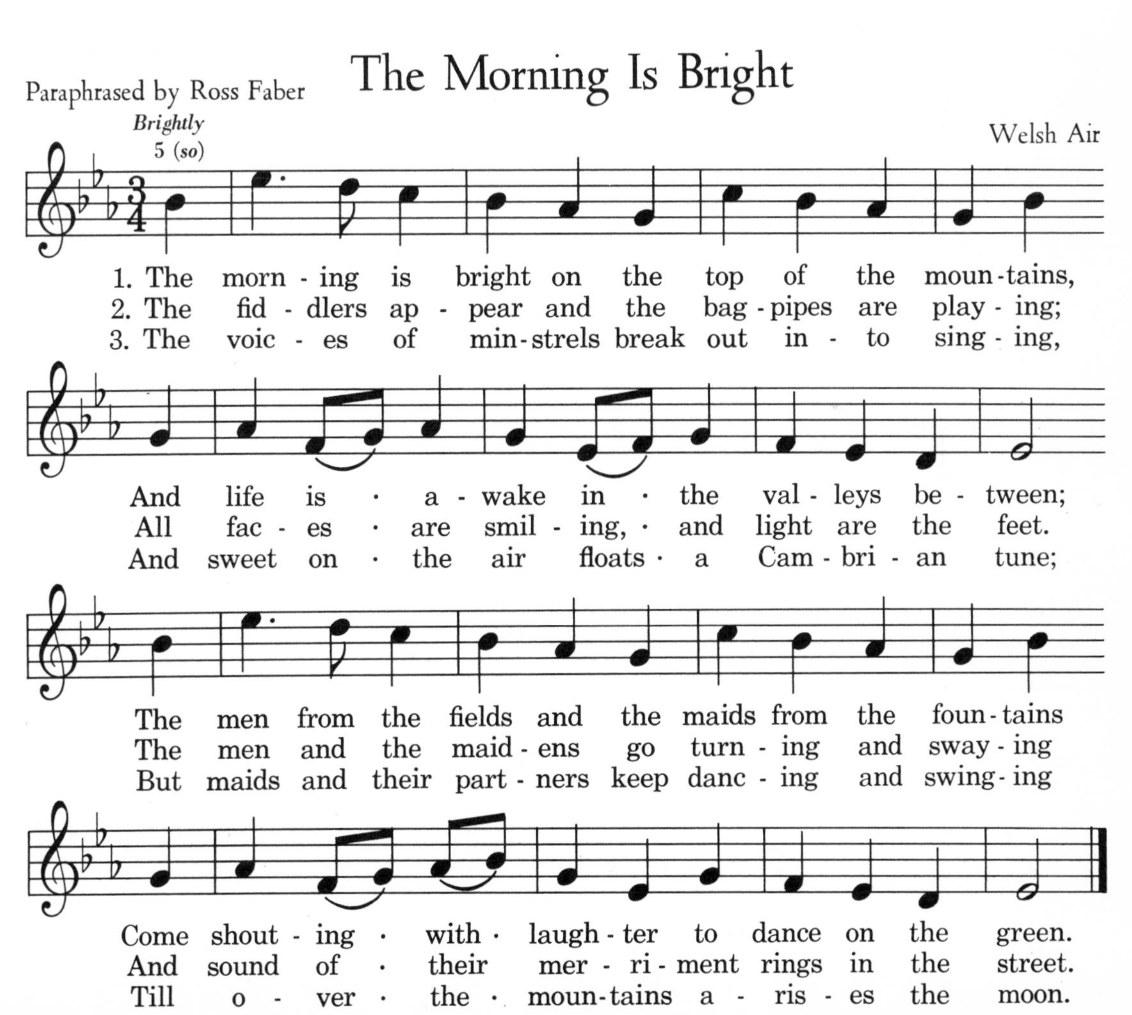
The Morning Is Bright
Paraphrased by Ross Faber
Brightly
5 (so)
Welsh Air
1. The morn - ing is bright on the top of the moun - tains,
2. The fid - dlers ap - pear and the bag - pipes are play - ing;
3. The voic - es of min - strels break out in - to sing - ing,
And life is · a - wake in · the val - leys be - tween;
All fac - es · are smil - ing, · and light are the feet.
And sweet on · the air floats · a Cam - bri - an tune;
The men from the fields and the maids from the foun - tains
The men and the maid - ens go turn - ing and sway - ing
But maids and their part - ners keep danc - ing and swing - ing
Come shout - ing · with · laugh - ter to dance on the green.
And sound of · their mer - ri - ment rings in the street.
Till o - ver · the · moun - tains a - ris - es the moon.

Day is here! Day is here, is here!
Arise, my son, lift thine eyes,
Day is here!

Pawnee Indian

The Sunrise Call

Zuñi Indian Song

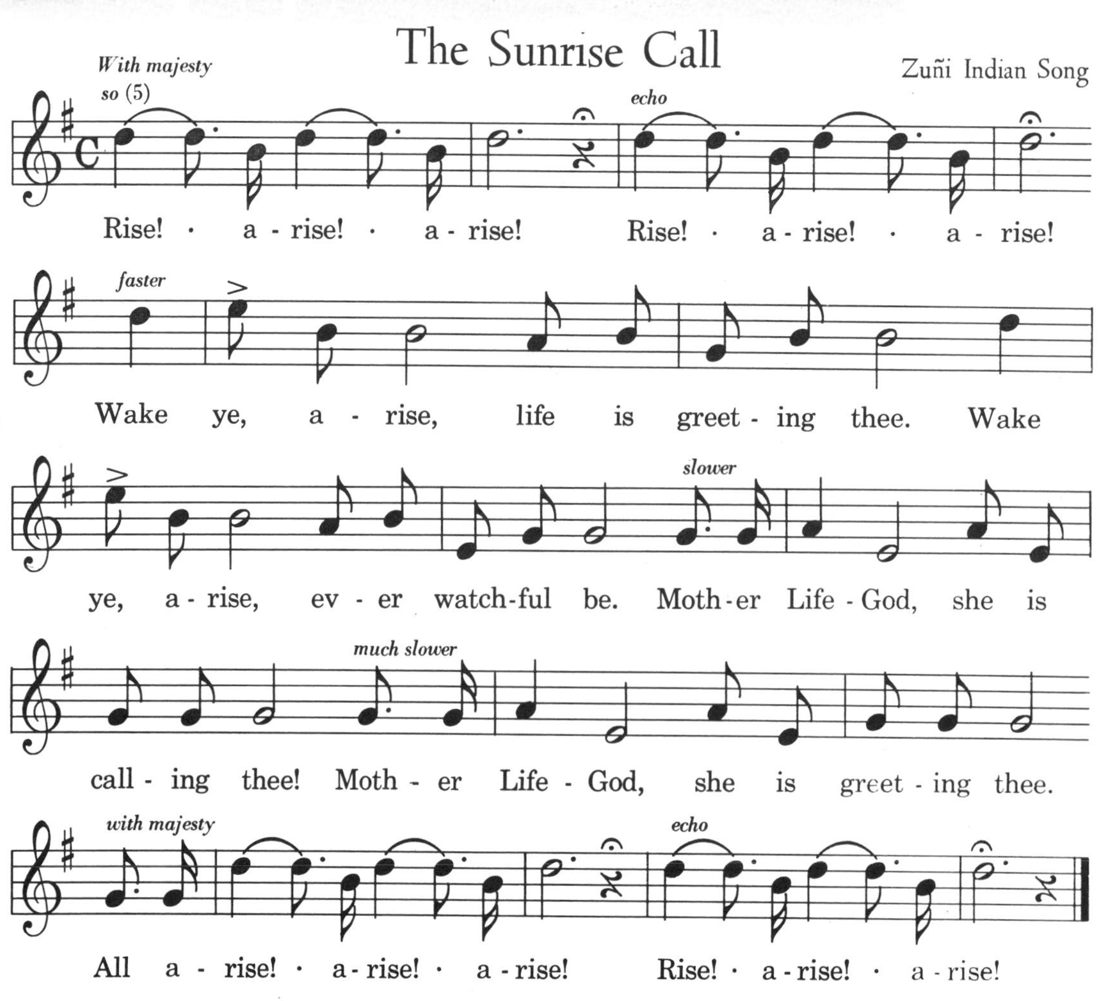

With majesty
so (5)
echo
Rise! · a - rise! · a - rise! Rise! · a - rise! · a - rise!
faster
Wake ye, a - rise, life is greet - ing thee. Wake
slower
ye, a - rise, ev - er watch-ful be. Moth - er Life - God, she is
much slower
call - ing thee! Moth - er Life - God, she is greet - ing thee.
with majesty
echo
All a - rise! · a - rise! · a - rise! Rise! · a - rise! · a - rise!

Listen to "Sunrise Dance," from *Suite Primeval*, Skilton. (Victor record.)

Sunset Song

Zuñi Indian Song
Slowly
mi
Good night to thee, fair · God-dess, We · thank thee for thy · bless-ing,
Good night to thee, fair · God - dess, We · thank thee for this · day.
with increased fervor
In glo - ry we be - hold thee At · ear - ly dawn a - gain.
softer
We thank thee for thy · bless - ing, To · be with us this · day,
gradually softer
This · day, we · thank thee · for this · day.

Listen to "Sunset," from *Grand Canyon Suite,* Grofe. (Victor or Columbia record.)

Deep in the Forest

Ethel Crowninshield

Ojibway Indian

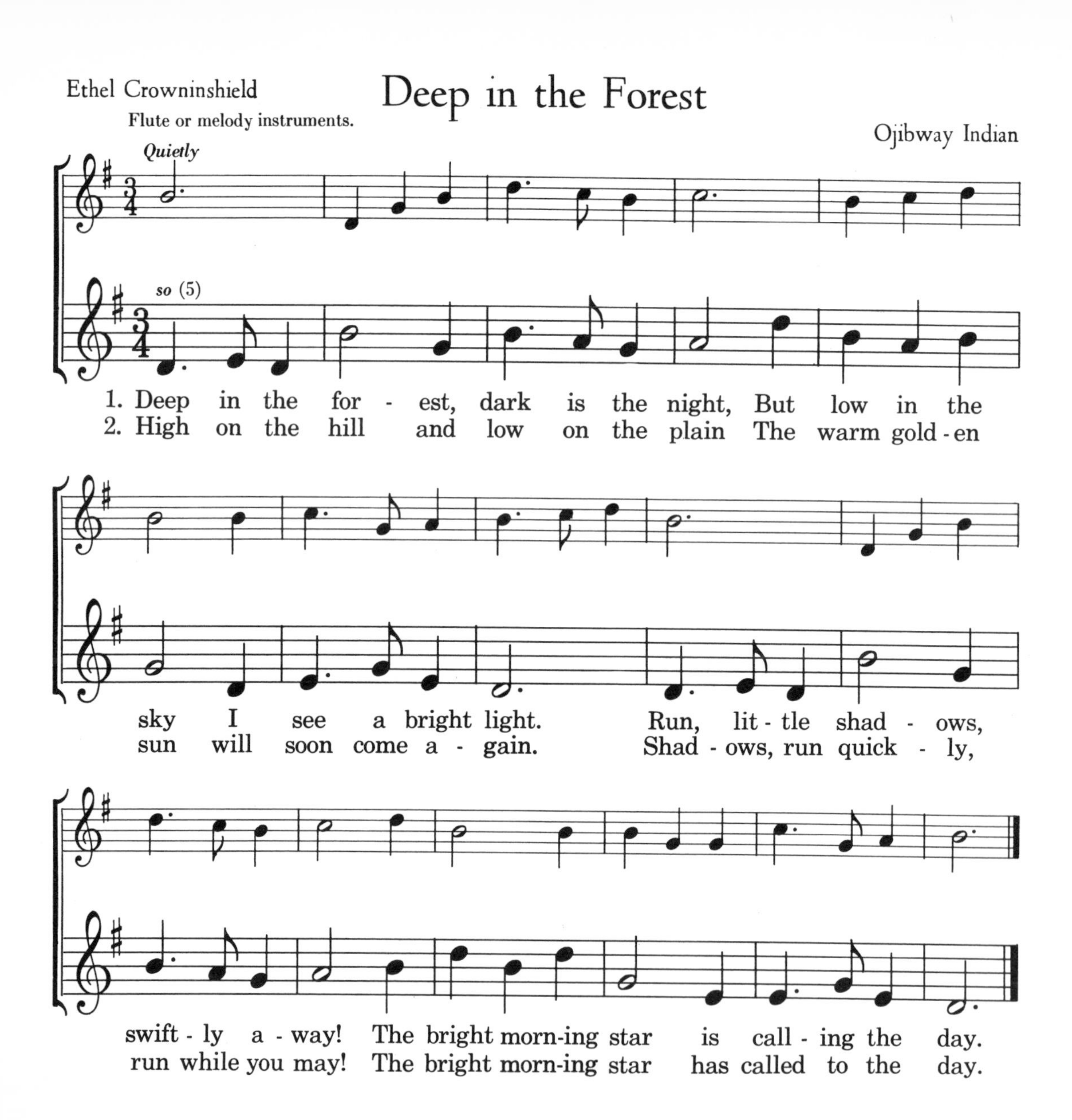
Flute or melody instruments.
Quietly
so (5)
1. Deep in the for - est, dark is the night, But low in the
2. High on the hill and low on the plain The warm gold - en
sky I see a bright light. Run, lit - tle shad - ows,
sun will soon come a - gain. Shad - ows, run quick - ly,
swift - ly a - way! The bright morn-ing star is call - ing the day.
run while you may! The bright morn-ing star has called to the day.

Evensong

Lynn Seeley

Selim Palmgren

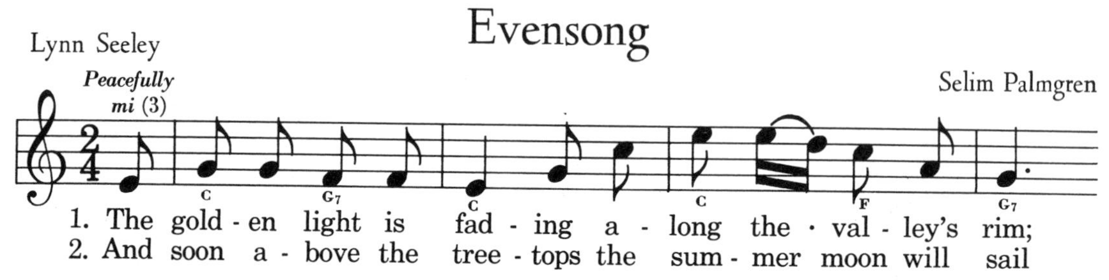
Peacefully
mi (3)
C G7 C C F G7
1. The gold - en light is fad - ing a - long the · val - ley's rim;
2. And soon a - bove the tree - tops the sum - mer moon will sail

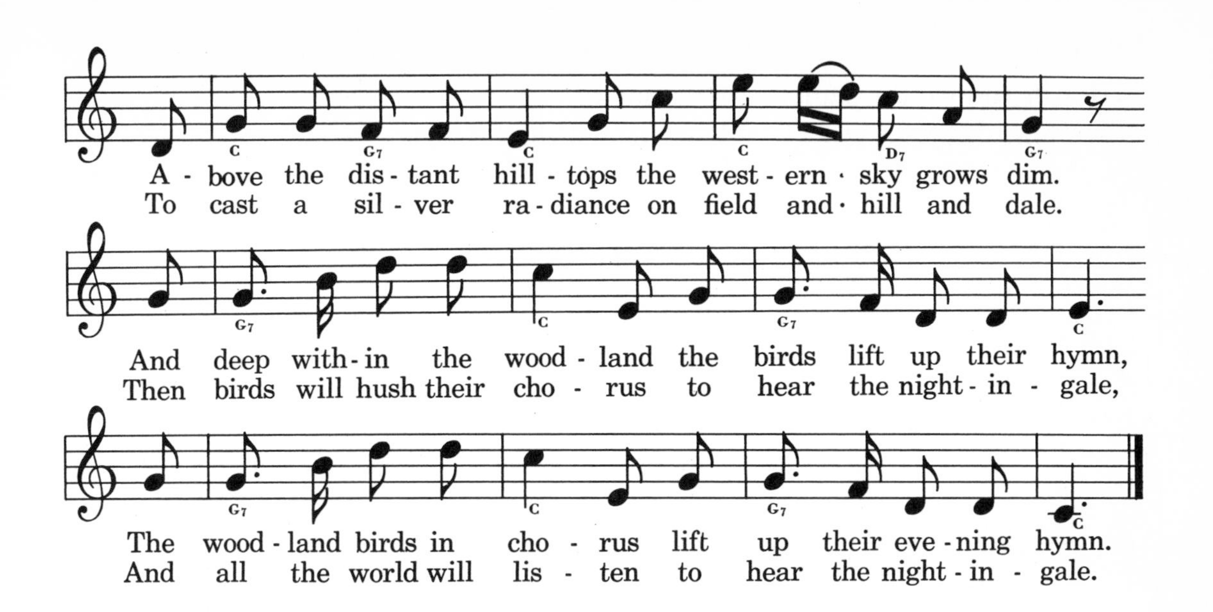
A - bove the dis - tant hill - tops the west - ern sky grows dim.
To cast a sil - ver ra - diance on field and hill and dale.
And deep with - in the wood - land the birds lift up their hymn,
Then birds will hush their cho - rus to hear the night - in - gale,
The wood - land birds in cho - rus lift up their eve - ning hymn.
And all the world will lis - ten to hear the night - in - gale.

Nancy Byrd Turner

Chinese Evening Song

Chinese Folk Tune

With expression
la
1. Tem - ple bells ring soft and clear Down the twi - light hill,
2. Birds are drow - sy in their nest, Slow the shad - ows creep,
softer
Dusk - y qui - et hill Where the shad - ows fill.
Tip - toe shad - ows creep, Dark is grow - ing deep.
Ling Foo, go to sleep, my dear, Lo - tus blooms are drift - ing near;
All the world has gone to rest, One fair star is in the west,
very soft
Night is on the hill; Tem - ple bells are still.
And a watch will keep. Ling Foo, go to sleep.

Listen to "In a Chinese Temple Garden," Ketelbey. (Victor record.)

Stars over snow,
And in the west a planet
Swinging below a star—
Look for a lovely thing and you will find it.
It is not far—
It never will be far.

Sara Teasdale

Translated by Emily M. Fingulin

The Planets

Czech Folk Song

Moderately
1 (do)
Sil-ver is the moon; Calm as the sea, Peace-ful, you ap-pear to
me. Gold-en is the sun, Warm and ra-diant too.
Oh, what can your mag-ic be? All things grow and need your rays
To gain e-ter-nal strength. May you ev-er shine on me.
Twin-kle, lit-tle star, Far a-way you are. Bring e-ter-nal peace on earth.
3

Listen to "Nocturne," from *Midsummer Night's Dream,* Mendelssohn. (Victor Listening Album Four.)

Little Star

L. E. Watters

Sweetly
1 (do)
1. O lit-tle star, so brave, so high, There you are shin-ing in the sky,
2. When I am lone-ly, lit-tle star, I see you twin-kling where you are;

While land and sea be - low in dark - ness lie.
And know you're watch-ing o'er me from a - far.
O-ver the sky your bright-ness gleams, Down-ward you send your ra-diant beams
Now through my win-dow shin-ing bright Spar-kles your friend-ly gold - en light
To light the night time, and to bring me dreams.
Till sleep comes o'er me. Lit - tle star, good night.
Moon and Her Children
Paraphrased from the German
by Rose Fyleman
Caroline Hammond
Quietly with motion
mi (3)
1. At mid-night in the sky, I see the moon pass by.
2. She guards her chil - dren dear, The stars that shine so clear.
She shines on field and cit - y, And kind she is and pret - ty;
The whole night long they stay there, And laugh and dance and play there,
She wears a roy - al dress Of sil - ver love - li - ness.
But when the dawn grows red She puts them all to bed.

Listen to "Clair de Lune," Debussy. (Victor Listening Album Five.)

Song on a Hilltop

Ethel E. Holmes

Josephine Knowles Kendel

Moderately
so
Oh, love - ly, love - ly, whose song had I heard— Love - ly, love - ly,
was it a bird? I looked and looked, but could - n't see A
accelerate
thing that could sing, ex - cept - ing me. I held my breath,
slower
shut my eyes tight, Stood still and lis - tened with all my might; And
softly
then I clapped my hands with glee For that song came from the heart of me!
joyfully

Wind and Water
Paraphrased by Ann Rolfe
Song of the Breezes
French
With swaying motion
3 (mi)
1 (do)
C G7 C G7 C G7 C G7 C G7 C C G7 G7 C G7 G7 C C G7 G7 C
1. For - est, a - wake, mur - mur - ing trees, Let your green arms rock in the breeze. Far from the sun, deep in the grove, Hear ev - 'ry bough whis - per and move.
2. Black-birds a - loft, pip - ing and clear, Sprin - kle their songs high in the air. Let the sweet tunes, mer - ry and gay, Drift on the wind far, far a - way.
CHORUS
O - pen wide, wood - land door; Pine trees sigh like waves on the shore. Through the leaves, through the ferns, Sum - mer wind waltz - es and turns.

Listen to "Tales from the Vienna Woods," Johann Strauss. (Victor record.)

Who Has Seen the Wind?

Christina Rossetti
L. E. Watters
With expression
1 (do)
Who has seen the wind? Nei - ther I nor you;
But when the leaves hang trem-bling, The wind is pass-ing through.
Who has seen the wind? Nei - ther you nor I;
But when the trees bow down their heads, The wind is pass - ing by.

Good-By

English version
by Christine Turner Curtis
Gracefully
so (5)
mi (3)
Filipino Folk Song
F
dm
gm
C7
1. The wind is in the co - coa palm, The tide runs high;
2. Oh, play your man - do - lin and sing A song for me
My ban - ca¹ waits up - on the sand; Good-by, Ra-quel, good- by.
Be - fore I jour - ney far a - way A-cross the deep blue sea!

[1] A Filipino boat.

A Boat, A Boat to Cross the Ferry

English Round

1. 5 (so)
2.
3.
A boat, a boat to cross the fer - ry, And we'll go o - ver
and be mer - ry, And as we float, sing hey down der - ry.

Come, Ye Maidens

Translated

Maori Canoe Song
Arranged by A. H. Pettitt

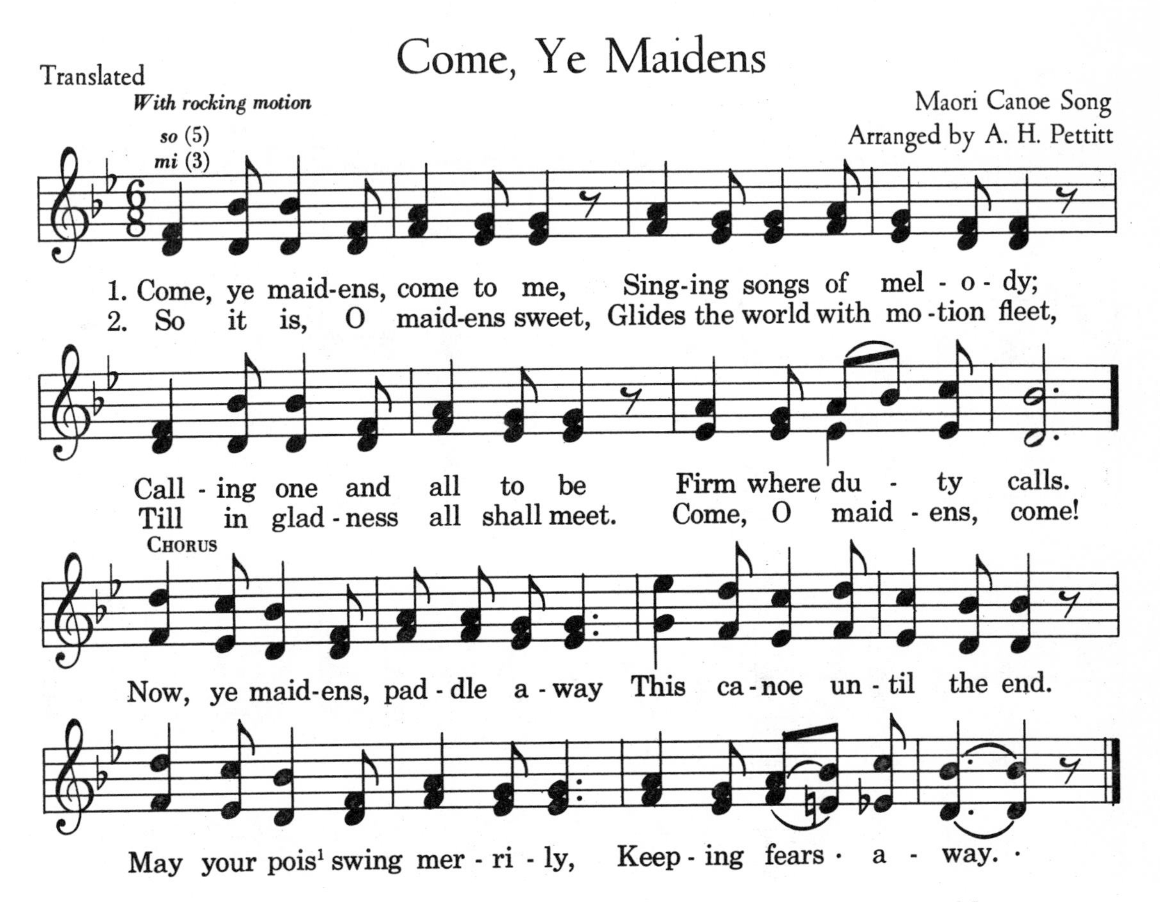
With rocking motion
so (5)
mi (3)
1. Come, ye maid-ens, come to me, Sing-ing songs of mel - o - dy;
2. So it is, O maid-ens sweet, Glides the world with mo-tion fleet,
Call - ing one and all to be Firm where du - ty calls.
Till in glad - ness all shall meet. Come, O maid - ens, come!
Chorus
Now, ye maid-ens, pad - dle a - way This ca-noe un - til the end.
May your pois[1] swing mer - ri - ly, Keep - ing fears · a - way. ·

[1]"*Poi*" balls are made from the leaves of a native plant and are attached to pieces of flax string. The swinging ball adds movement to the rhythm of the singing. The Maori are natives of New Zealand.

Lightly Row

Traditional Song

5 (so)
3 (mi)
Light-ly row, light-ly row, O'er the shin-ing waves we go;
Smooth-ly glide, smooth-ly glide On the si-lent tide.
Let the winds and wa-ters be Still and calm and clear to see;
Sing and float, sing and float In our lit-tle boat.

One of you play this on the piano while the others sing.
Listen to "En Bateau" (Boating), Debussy. (Victor or Columbia record.)

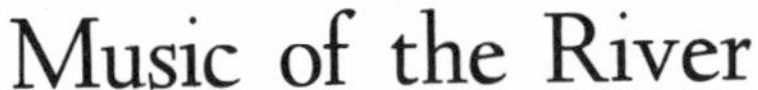
Music of the River

Stanley Martin
Smoothly
Lauretta V. Sweesy
mi (3)
1. Flow - ing, on - ward go;
2. Riv - er, on - ward go;
do (1)
F F C7 C7
1. Gen - tle riv - er, qui - et riv - er, on - ward go.
2. Peace - ful riv - er, no - ble riv - er, broad and strong,
Sea - ward, sing - ing slow;
Sea - ward, sing - ing free;
C7 C7 C7 F
Tell us tales of old ad - ven - tures as you flow.
Sing a song of no - ble meas - ure, deep and long.
Mur - mur in my dream,
Sing sweet songs for me,
F F gm gm
Tell us tales of new ad - ven - tures yon - der that a - wait,
Stead - y keep your on - ward flow - ing; it shall end - ed be,
Songs of long a - go.
Songs of joy to be.
F gm C7 F
When you pass with sing - ing through the far - off sea - ward gate.
When at last you flow in - to some hap - py shin - ing sea.

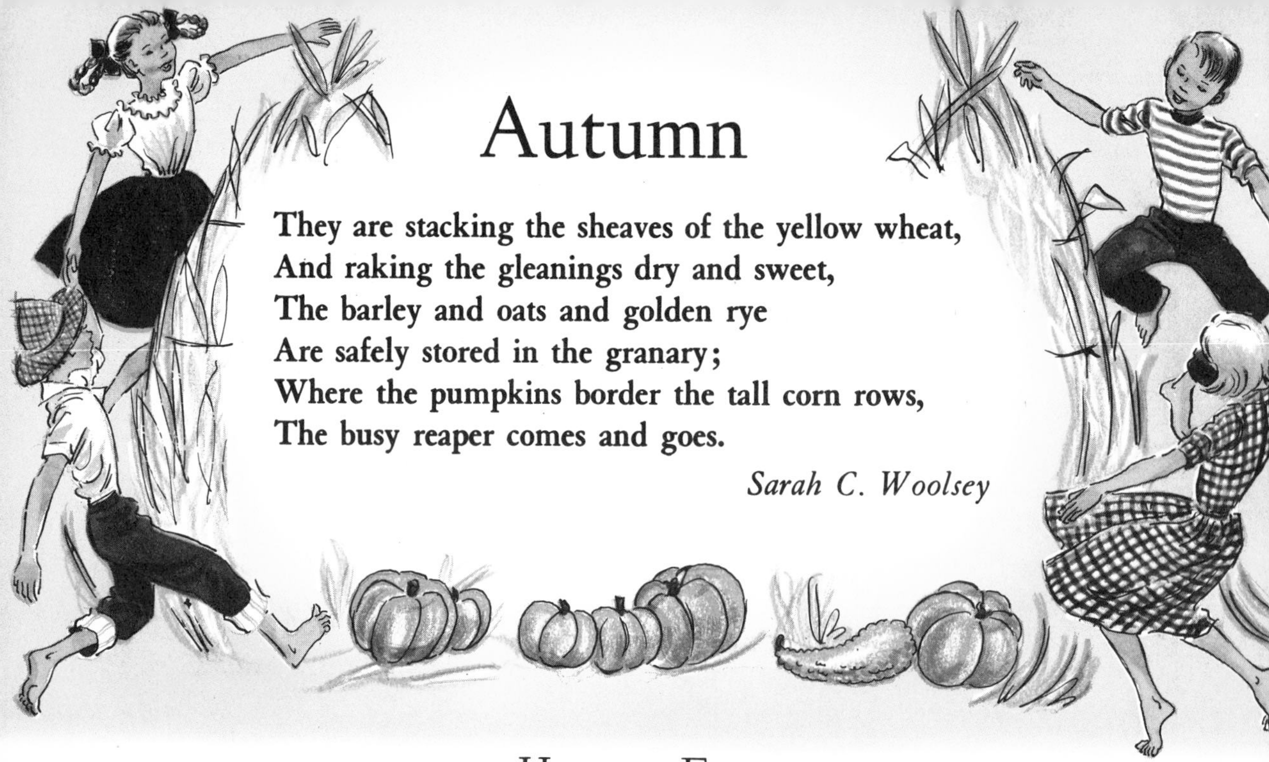

Autumn

They are stacking the sheaves of the yellow wheat,
And raking the gleanings dry and sweet,
The barley and oats and golden rye
Are safely stored in the granary;
Where the pumpkins border the tall corn rows,
The busy reaper comes and goes.

Sarah C. Woolsey

Harvest Fun

With marked rhythm — Henry M. Halvorson

5 (so)

What fun we have at har - vest time, With gold- en grain we work all day;

Fine

But when the eve-ning sun has set, We sing and dance the night a-way.

1. The wag- ons creak - y, creak-y, creak, The crick - ets cheep - y, cheep- y, cheep,
2. The cooks, they stew and stew and stew, The har-vest hands, they eat and eat;

ritard
D.C. al Fine

The reap-ers squeak-y, squeak-y, squeak, The lit-tlebirds go tweet, tweet, tweet.
At night they dance and dance and dance While lit-tle birds do sleep, sleep, sleep.

When the Chestnut Leaves Were Falling

English version by Luther Wilde

Spanish Folk Song

Not too slow
5 (so)
3 (mi)
F C7 F F
1. When the chest - nut leaves were fall - ing, 'Ni - ta was tend - ing her sheep, · By the brook she saw a gyp - sy Look - ing in the wa - ter deep. ·
2. Then he raised his eyes to beg her, "Give me a drink if you will." · 'Ni - ta made a cup of rush - es And the gyp - sy drank his fill. ·
3. When the chest - nut leaves were fall - ing, 'Ni - ta heard mel - o - dy float, · As the gyp - sy whis - tled sweet - ly Like a song - bird, note for note. ·
C7 C7
F D7 gm C7 F

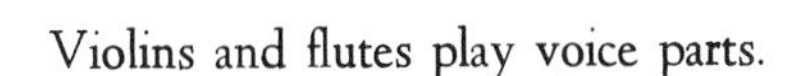
Violins and flutes play voice parts.

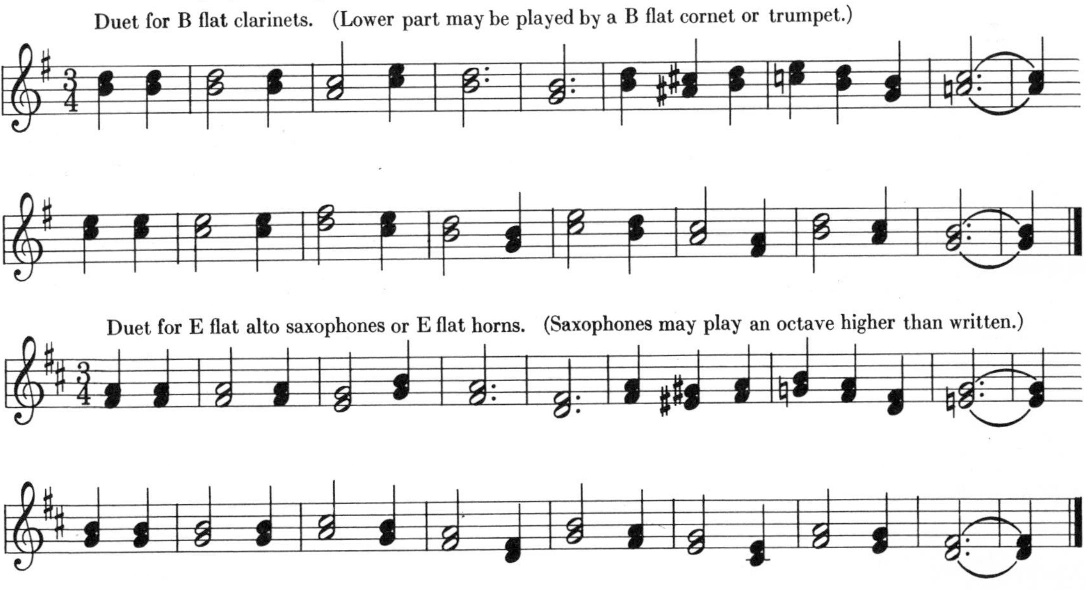
Duet for B flat clarinets. (Lower part may be played by a B flat cornet or trumpet.)
Duet for E flat alto saxophones or E flat horns. (Saxophones may play an octave higher than written.)

Autumn Is a Painter
Christine Turner Curtis
Somewhat chantlike
George Frederick McKay
1 (do)
When au-tumn o - pens her box of paints She choos-es yel - low and
brown and red, And all night long her brush - es fly To
more lyric
col - or branch-es o - ver - head. She paints the ma-ples crim-son fire A -
long the mead - ow and through the town. She turns a birch to
pal - est gold, And splash - es oaks with red and brown. And
chantlike
when her won - der work is done, Be - hold a for - est of
152

more lyric
burn-ing light! And out we go to gath-er boughs To
flame in win-dows day and night, To flame in win-dows day and night.
2

Indian Summer

Ross Faber

Harry H. Schyde

Languidly
so (5)
mi (3)
1. La-zy In-dian sum-mer days Shim-mer in a gold-en haze;
2. All the air is soft and still, Si-lence sleeps on field and hill;
Drow-sy crick-ets, one by one, Creep in-to the noon-day sun;
One can hear the small-est sound, A-corns drop-ping to the ground;
Spi-ders loop their sil-ver threads All a-long the gar-den beds;
Trees that heave a gen-tle sigh, Wild birds pass-ing in the sky;
And the sky is like a shell Shed-ding down a dream-y spell.
La-zy In-dian sum-mer days Shim-mer in a gold-en haze.

Winter

Swing! Swing! Swing!
Over the crystal ice!
Where the sunbeam flashes and falls apart
Into prisms of color that dance and dart,
And down below
The fishes go
As they see our skates gleam to and fro,
Swinging, ringing, singing,
Over the good green ice!

Christopher Morley

Christine Turner Curtis
With graceful motion
The Skaters
Emil Waldteufel
3 (mi)
Skat - ers, a - way! Glide, glide and sway,
Skat - ers, fly on, Light as the swan.
Dart - ing and fly - ing like gulls at play.
Skate till the pale win - ter sun is gone.
Fine
On your sil - ver - y skates you go swirl - ing, swirl - ing,
O - ver the ice mad - ly whirl - ing, whirl - ing,
Scarves in the breez - es un - furl - ing, furl - ing.

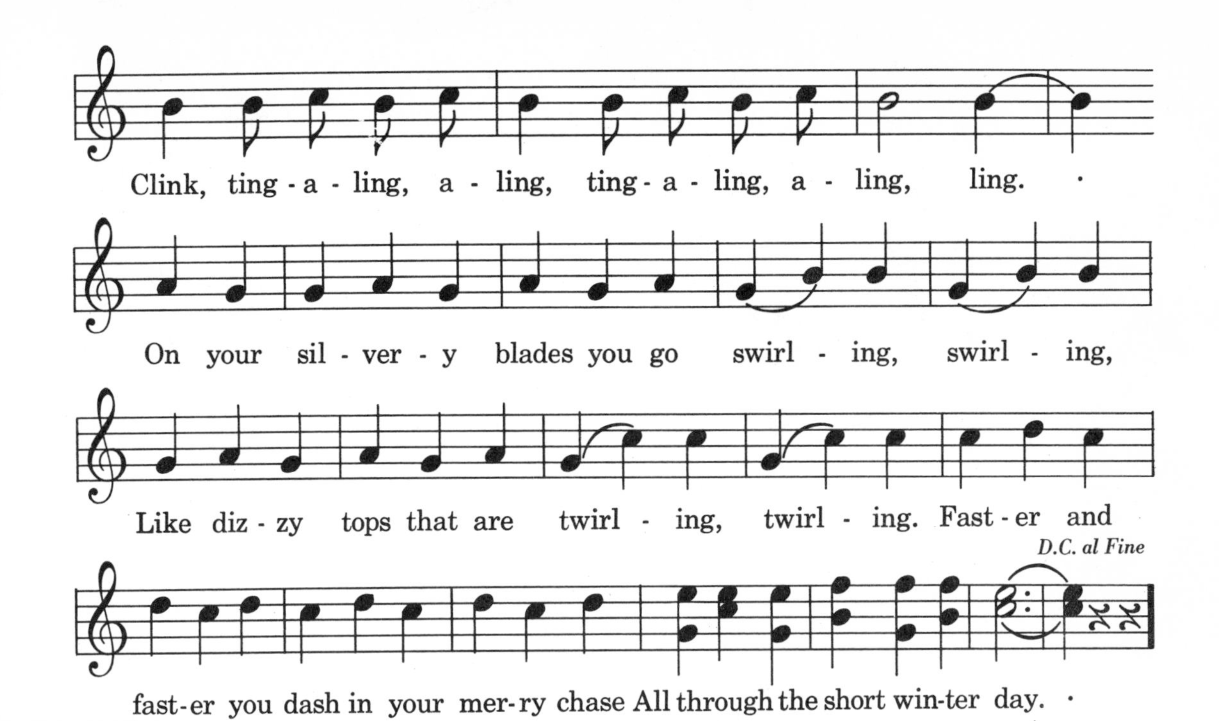
Clink, ting - a - ling, a - ling, ting - a - ling, a - ling, ling.
On your sil - ver - y blades you go swirl - ing, swirl - ing,
Like diz - zy tops that are twirl - ing, twirl - ing. Fast - er and
D.C. al Fine
fast-er you dash in your mer-ry chase All through the short win-ter day.

Listen to "The Skaters-Waltz," Waldteufel. (Victor Rhythm Album Four.)

Signs of Winter

Lynn Seeley

L. E. Watters

Not too slow

5 (*so*)
3 (*mi*)

1. The frost is on the fur - row, The for - est trees are bare.
2. The yel - low fox fore - tell - ing King Win-ter's cold white hand,
3. The small birds fly to the thick - et, In hid-ing sits the quail;

The gray mole seeks his bur - row, And home-ward limps the hare.
Digs deep his win - ter dwell - ing With - in the froz - en land.
The bear shuts up his wick - et And sleeps thru storm and gale.

Give Us the Wintertime

Christine Turner Curtis

Robert W. Gibb

With spirit

3 (*mi*)

1. Give us the rous - ing win - ter, Set-ting the cheeks a - glow;
2. Give us the moon of win - ter, Whit-er than froz - en pearl,

Give us the rous-ing storm wind O-ver the pas-tures blow-ing and snow-ing.
Give us the ice-bound riv - er Cov-ered with skat-ers curl-ing and twirl-ing.

On with the skis and snow - shoes, Moun-tains and hills we'll climb,
Give us the sound of sleigh - bells Ring - ing a frost - y chime,

What though they freeze us, bliz-zards can please us; Give us the win - ter - time.
Though it be snow - y, i - cy and blow - y; Give us the win - ter - time.

The Sleighride

Sprightly
so
N. Lincoln
G G D7 G
1. Oh, swift we go o'er shin-ing snow When moon-beams spar - kle bright;
2. On win-try night, when hearts are light, What fun we have as we go.
G G D7 A7 D7
While hoofs keep time to mu-sic's chime As mer - ri - ly goes the night.
With laugh and song we glide a - long A - cross the drift - ing snow.
Chorus
G G
So mer - ri - ly, mer - ri - ly, mer - ri - ly, mer - ri - ly,
D7 G G
Mer - ri - ly on we go, we go; So mer - ri - ly, mer - ri - ly,
G D7 G
mer - ri - ly, mer - ri - ly, Mer - ri - ly on we go.

Listen to "The Sleigh Ride," Anderson. (Victor record.)

Listen to "In a Three-Horse Sleigh" (Troika en Traineaux), Tchaikovsky. (Victor record.)

Spring

A little bit of blowing,
A little bit of snowing,
A little bit of growing
And crocuses will show!

A little bit of sleeting,
A little bit of rain,
The blue, blue sky for greeting
A snowdrop come again!

And every frozen hillside
Its gift of grass will bring,
And every day of winter
Another day of spring.

Carolyn Sherwin Bailey

Annette Wynne[1]

I Heard It in the Valley

Charles Leonhard

Happily
mi (3)

F
B♭
F

I heard it in the val - ley, I heard it in the glen.

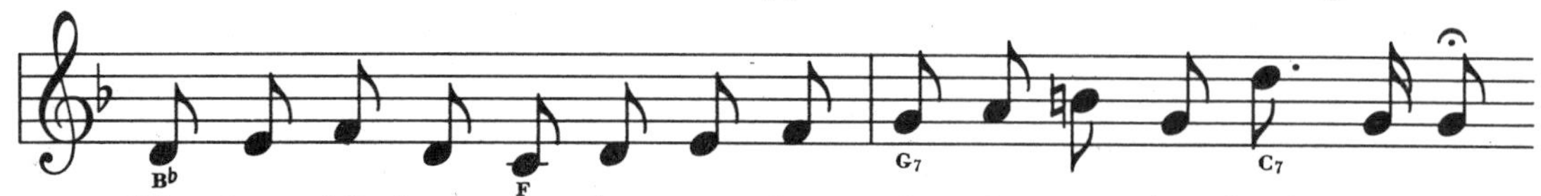
B♭
F
G7
C7

Lis - ten, chil - dren, sure - ly, sure - ly, spring is com - ing back a - gain.

F
D7
gm

I heard it in the val - ley, I heard the wa - ters start.

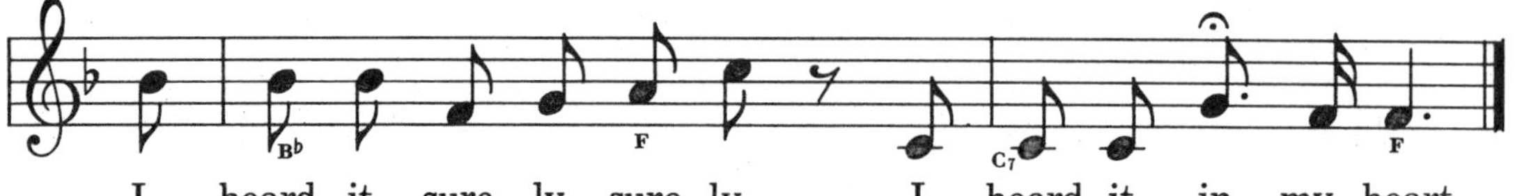
B♭
F
C7
F

I heard it sure - ly, sure - ly. I heard it in my heart.

Listen to "To Spring," Grieg. (Victor Listening Album Six.)

[1]Reprinted by permission of the publisher, J. B. Lippincott Company, from *All Through the Year* by Annette Wynne. Copyright, 1932, by Annette Wynne.

Spring Has Come

Translated by Margareta Wassali
Swiss Folk Song
Joyfully
so (5) mi (3)
1. Now spring-time is here and the soft · winds blow To melt from the
2. The herds-man looks up at the blue · spring sky; He shouts and he
moun-tains the ice and the snow. The cuck - oo is call - ing in
sings to the moun - tains high. "Good - by, lit - tle val - ley, good-
vales be - low To say that this is so. · Yo ho - lee, ho - lee,
by, good - by," You hear his lust - y cry. · Yo ho - lee, ho - lee,
Yo ho - lee
Yo ho - lee
ho - la, lee - ho, Up in - to the moun-tains the cows will go. Yo
ho - la, lee - ho, Up in - to the Alps where the grass - es grow. Yo
ho. · Yo ho - lee, ho - lee ho.
ho. · Yo ho - lee, ho - lee ho.
ho - lee, ho - lee, ho - la, lee - ho, Up to the moun - tains go. ·
ho - lee, ho - lee, ho - la, lee - ho, Up to the Alps we'll go. ·
Yo ho - lee ho, Yo ho, yo ho.
Yo ho - lee ho, Yo ho, yo ho.

In mountainous countries like Switzerland and Norway it is customary to herd cattle in the upland meadows all summer.

Spring Song

Ludwig Christoph Hölty
Translated by Christine Turner Curtis

Franz Schubert
Adapted and arranged by L. E. Watters

Violin or flute.
Cheerfully
mi (3)

1. The vales are green and blue the skies, The cow - slips o - pen their
2. Come out to see the love - ly May, With bud - ding branch-es and

yel - low eyes; And blue-bells in · the woods are seen.
blos - som-spray, And green-ing fields on ev - 'ry hand.

The mead - ows wear a dew - y sheen, With dia-monds fit to
For God · has giv - en His · com-mand, And set with beau-ty

deck a queen, With dia-monds fit to deck a · queen.
all the land, And set with beau-ty all the · land.

Trout Brook in Spring

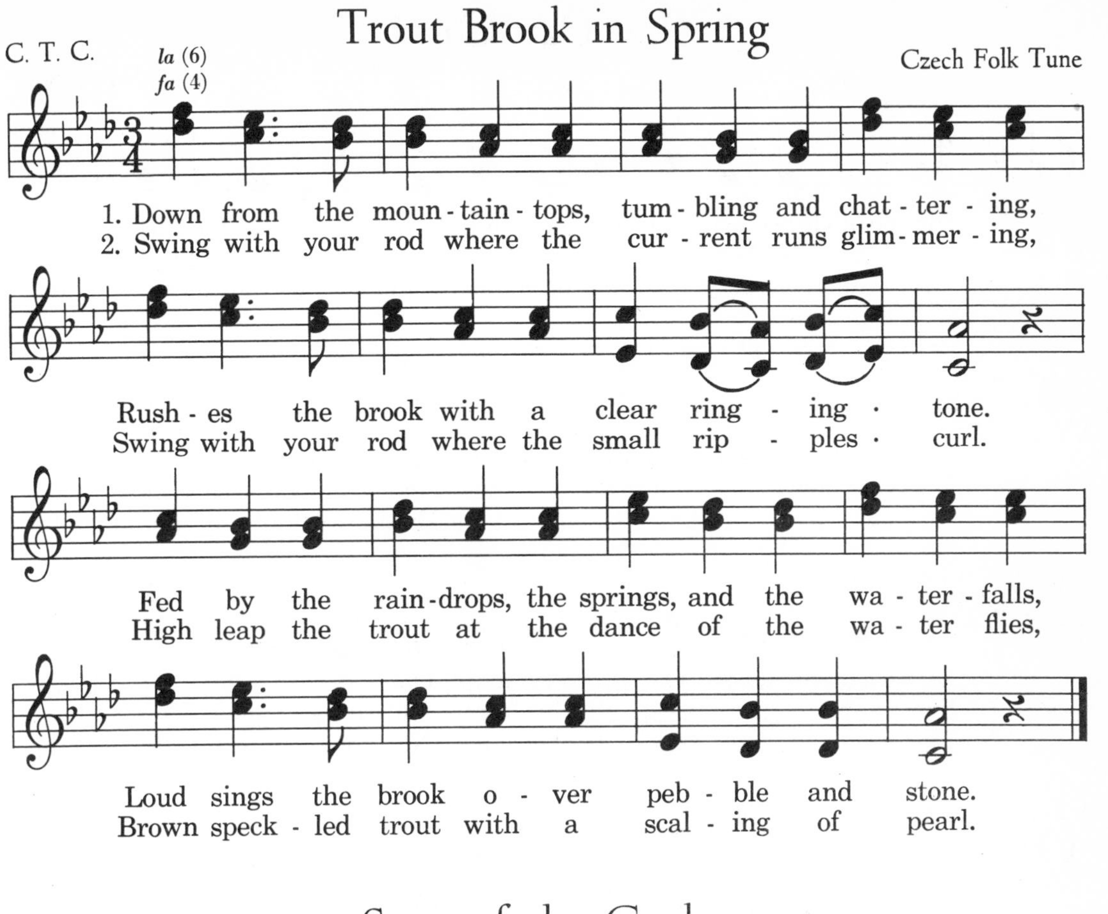
C. T. C.
Czech Folk Tune
la (6)
fa (4)
1. Down from the moun-tain-tops, tum-bling and chat-ter-ing,
2. Swing with your rod where the cur-rent runs glim-mer-ing,
Rush-es the brook with a clear ring-ing tone.
Swing with your rod where the small rip-ples curl.
Fed by the rain-drops, the springs, and the wa-ter-falls,
High leap the trout at the dance of the wa-ter flies,
Loud sings the brook o-ver peb-ble and stone.
Brown speck-led trout with a scal-ing of pearl.

Song of the Cuckoo

Adapted by Susanna Myers
German Folk Song
Lightly so (5)
mi (3)
1. Cuck-oo, cuck-oo! Spring-time is here. Sing of the flow-ers,
2. Cuck-oo, cuck-oo! Sing it a-gain, Morn-ing and eve-ning,
sun-shine and show-ers. Cuck-oo, cuck-oo! Spring-time is here.
eve-ning and morn-ing. Cuck-oo, cuck-oo! Sing it a-gain.

Listen to "Cuckoo in the Woods," from *Carnival of Animals,* Saint-Saëns. (Victor record.)

Listen to cuckoo calls in "Toy Symphony," Haydn. (Victor Listening Album Three.)

May Day Carol

Traditional

English Folk Song

With expression
so (5)

1. The moon shines bright, the stars give light A lit - tle be - fore 'tis day.
2. If not a bowl of your sweet cream A beak-er to bring you cheer,
3. A branch of may I brought you here And here at your door I stand.

Our heav'n-ly Fa-ther, He called to us And He bade us wake and pray.
For God knows if a-gain we shall meet For the may-ing time next year.
'Tis but a sprout, but well bud-ded out By the work of our Lord's hand.

A - wake, a - wake, O pret - ty maid, Out of your drow-sy dream,
I've been a - ram - bling all this night And some time of this day,
My song is done and I'll be gone, No long - er can I stay.

And step in - to your dair - y house And fetch a bowl of cream.
And now re - turn - ing back I come With branch-es of the may.
God bless you all, both great and small, And send a joy - ful May.

The Lily Princess

Unknown (Japanese)

la

Down from her dain - ty head The Lil - y Prin - cess

light - ly drops A spid - er's air - y thread.

Bluebonnets

J. E. G.

With a swaying motion

James E. Green

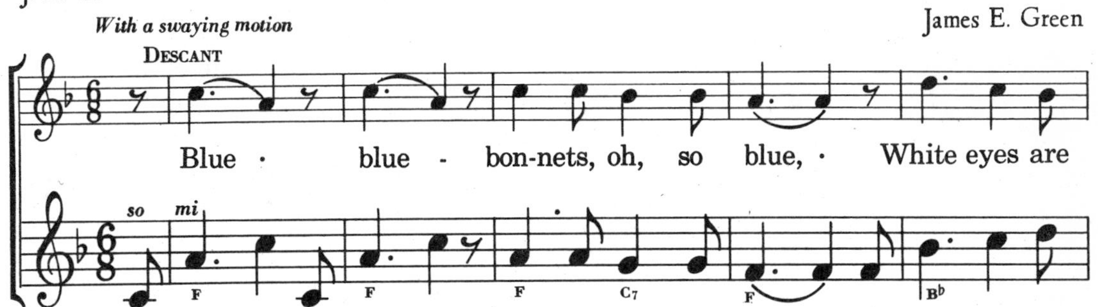
DESCANT
Blue · blue - bon-nets, oh, so blue, · White eyes are
so mi
F F F C7 F Bb
Blue-bon-nets, blue-bon-nets with your coats so blue, · Your white eyes are

shin-ing through dew. · Doll - y, doll - y of-fered for the
F G7 C7 F F F C7
shin- ing through the sil-v'ry dew. · I know you're a doll-y of-fered for the

rain, · Tex - as wears blue · · blue - bon - nets in the spring. ·
F Bb F G7 F C7 F
rain, · I know you'll re - turn a - gain to Tex - as in the spring. ·

This song is about an old legend in Texas. Many years ago the Tejas Indians were worried because a long, dry spell was leaving their fields bare and forest animals scarce.

None of the sacrifices they made to the rain gods brought results until a little Indian princess donated her most precious possession, her only doll. It had been made by her brother from a bluebird's feathers, white chalk, red clay, and green leaves.

The morning after she offered her doll as a sacrifice, the tribe awoke to find that life-giving rains had sprinkled the fields with thousands of blossoming bluebonnets.

Creatures Great and Small

Knowledge never learned of schools,
Of the wild bee's morning chase,
Of the wild flower's time and place,
Flight of fowl and habitude
Of the tenants of the wood.

John Greenleaf Whittier

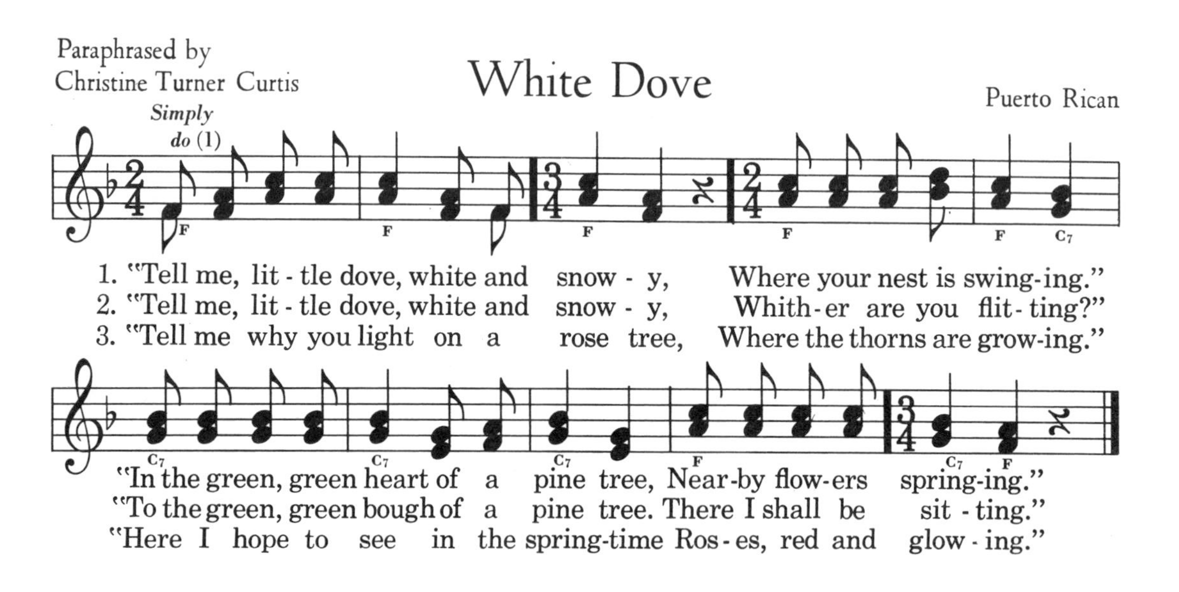

Paraphrased by
Christine Turner Curtis
White Dove
Puerto Rican
Simply
do (1)
F F F F F C7
1. "Tell me, lit - tle dove, white and snow - y, Where your nest is swing-ing."
2. "Tell me, lit - tle dove, white and snow - y, Whith-er are you flit - ting?"
3. "Tell me why you light on a rose tree, Where the thorns are grow-ing."
C7 C7 C7 F C7 F
"In the green, green heart of a pine tree, Near-by flow-ers spring-ing."
"To the green, green bough of a pine tree. There I shall be sit - ting."
"Here I hope to see in the spring-time Ros - es, red and glow - ing."

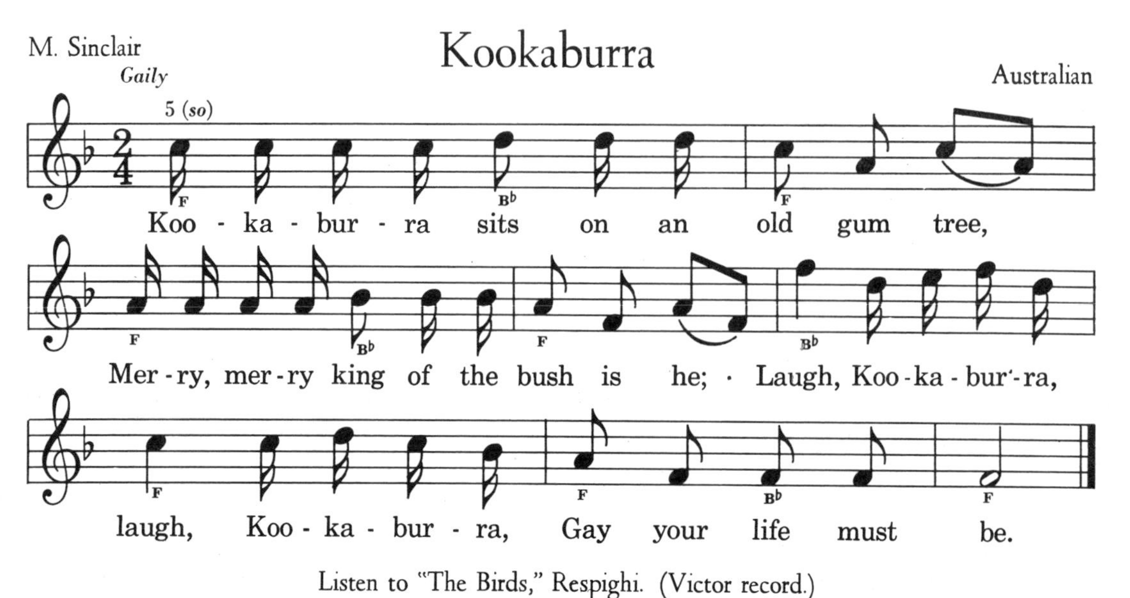

M. Sinclair
Kookaburra
Australian
Gaily
5 (so)
F B♭ F
Koo - ka - bur - ra sits on an old gum tree,
F B♭ F B♭
Mer - ry, mer - ry king of the bush is he; Laugh, Koo - ka - bur - ra,
F F B♭ F
laugh, Koo - ka - bur - ra, Gay your life must be.

Listen to "The Birds," Respighi. (Victor record.)

A Golden Cage Was Hanging

Translated

Mexican Folk Song

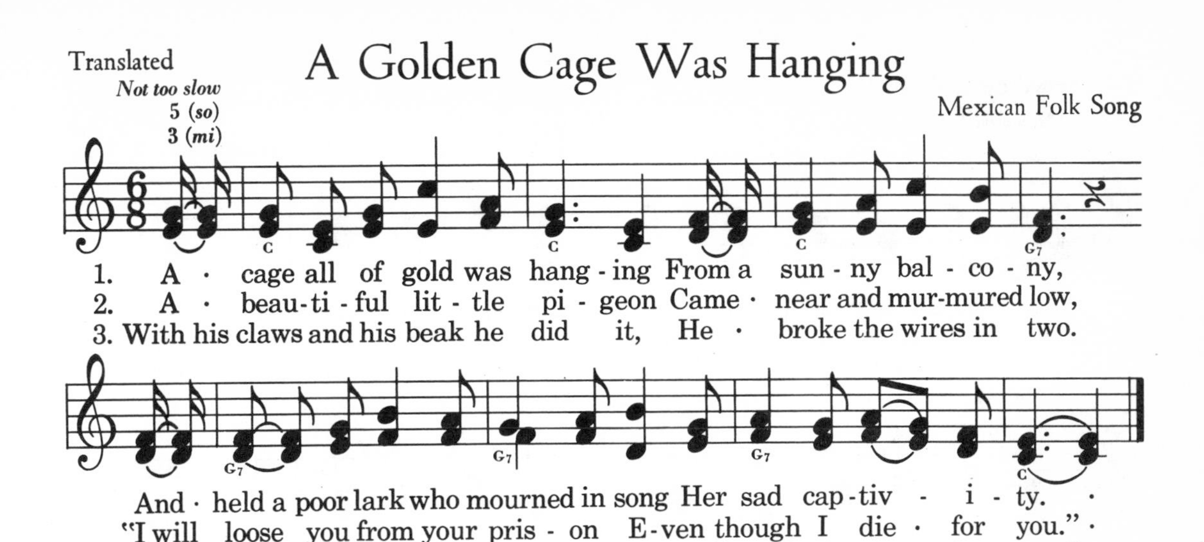
Not too slow
5 (so)
3 (mi)
C
G7
1. A · cage all of gold was hang - ing From a sun - ny bal - co - ny,
2. A · beau - ti - ful lit - tle pi - geon Came · near and mur-mured low,
3. With his claws and his beak he did it, He · broke the wires in two.
And · held a poor lark who mourned in song Her sad cap - tiv - i - ty. ·
"I will loose you from your pris - on E - ven though I die · for you." ·
"I will loose you from your pris - on E - ven though I die · for you." ·

Nightingale in the Wood

Translated by Christine Turner Curtis

Alsatian Folk Song

Gracefully
so (5)
1. Night - in - gale from the thick - et call - ing, Voice of night and
2. Night - in - gale, when the moon is shin - ing, Dip your beak · in
shad - ows fall - ing, From the val - leys deep · and · wild, ·
wa - ters twin - ing; From the cur - rent pluck · a · star, ·
Float your tones, · so mel - low and so mild, ·
Bear it to · my love who dwells a - far, ·
Night - in - gale, night - in - gale, na - ture's child. ·
Night - in - gale, night - in - gale, bear it a - far. ·

Lorita

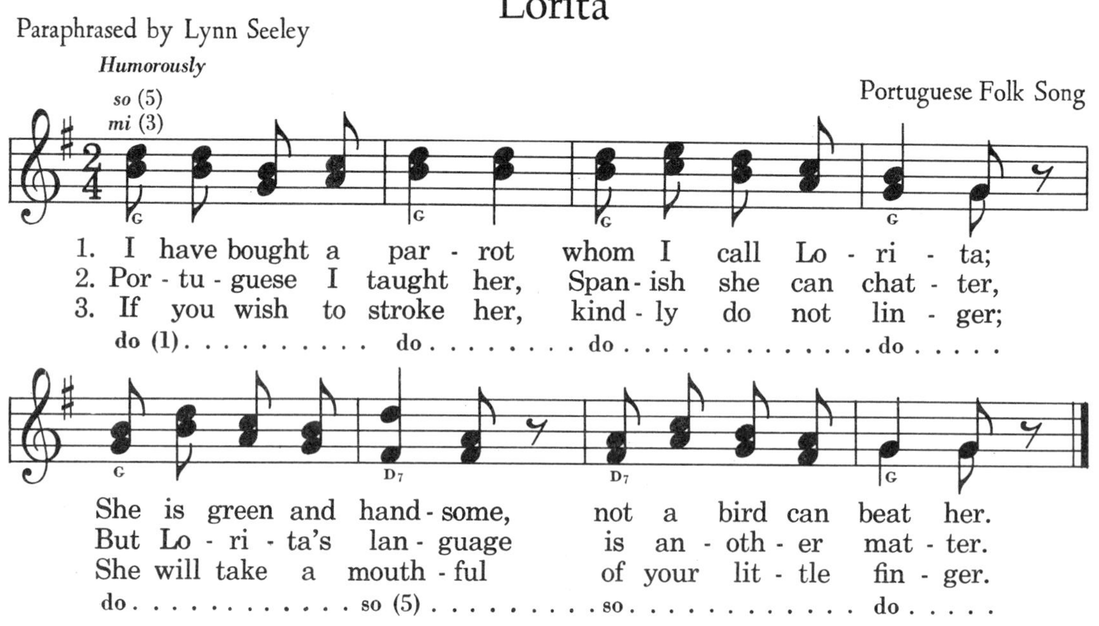
Paraphrased by Lynn Seeley
Humorously
Portuguese Folk Song
so (5)
mi (3)
G G G G
1. I have bought a par - rot whom I call Lo - ri - ta;
2. Por - tu - guese I taught her, Span - ish she can chat - ter,
3. If you wish to stroke her, kind - ly do not lin - ger;
do (1) . . . . do . . . . do . . . . do . . . . .
G D7 D7 G
She is green and hand - some, not a bird can beat her.
But Lo - ri - ta's lan - guage is an - oth - er mat - ter.
She will take a mouth - ful of your lit - tle fin - ger.
do . . . . so (5) . . . . so . . . . do . . . . .

Lone Dog
Irene Rutherford McLeod
With vigor
John Breidon
so (5)
F dm gm C7
I'm a lean dog, a keen dog, a wild dog, and lone;
F dm G7 C
I'm a rough dog, a tough dog, hunt - ing on my own;
dm gm C7
I'm a bad dog, a mad dog, teas - ing sil - ly sheep;
Bb F F C7 F
I love to sit and bay the moon, to keep the folks from sleep.

Sepp Has a Little Hen

Translated by Margareta Wassali

Swiss Folk Song

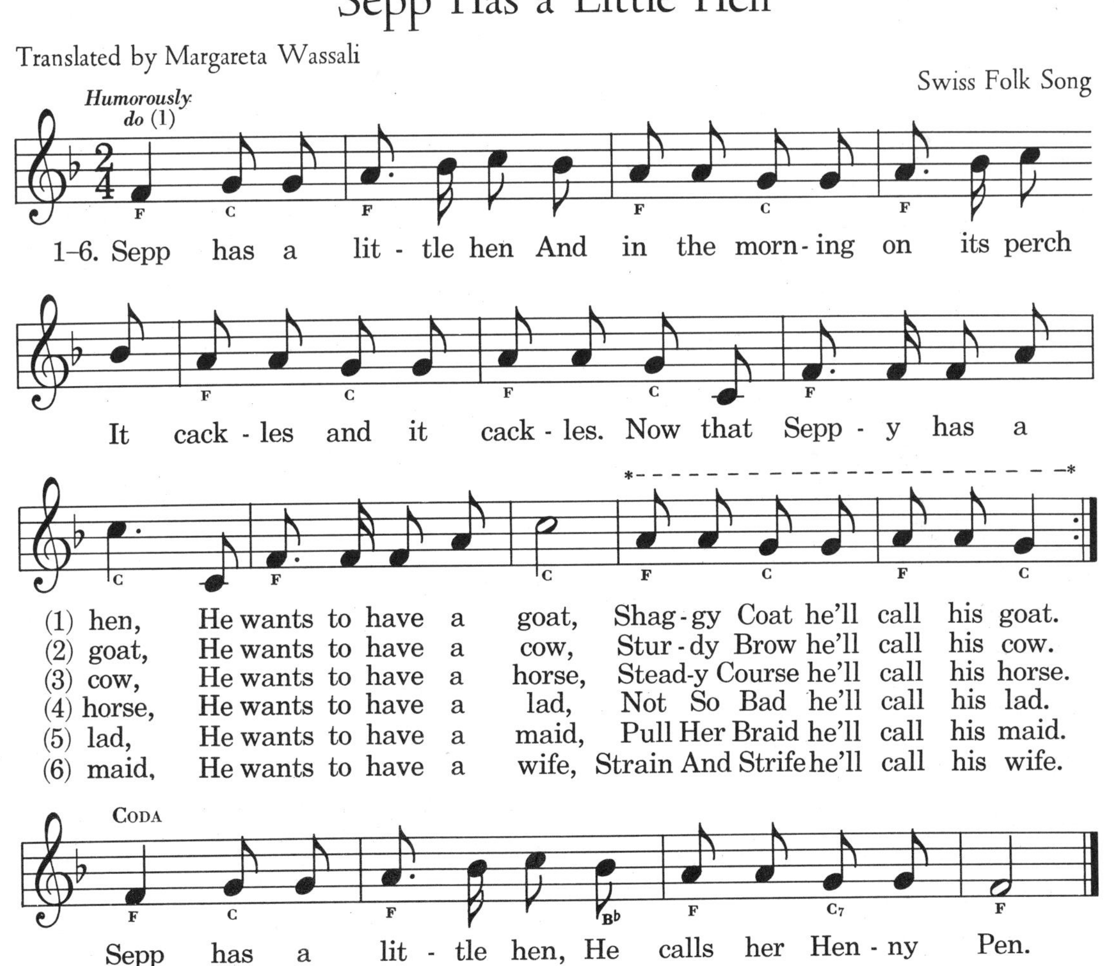
Humorously
do (1)
1–6. Sepp has a lit - tle hen And in the morn - ing on its perch
It cack - les and it cack - les. Now that Sepp - y has a
(1) hen, He wants to have a goat, Shag - gy Coat he'll call his goat.
(2) goat, He wants to have a cow, Stur - dy Brow he'll call his cow.
(3) cow, He wants to have a horse, Stead-y Course he'll call his horse.
(4) horse, He wants to have a lad, Not So Bad he'll call his lad.
(5) lad, He wants to have a maid, Pull Her Braid he'll call his maid.
(6) maid, He wants to have a wife, Strain And Strife he'll call his wife.
Coda
Sepp has a lit - tle hen, He calls her Hen - ny Pen.

In the second through the sixth stanza repeat the last two measures (*) of all the previous stanzas.

Tuku, Tuku, Tuu I'm Calling[1]

English text by Jean Teslof

Finnish Folk Song

Playfully
la

Tu-ku, tu-ku, tuu I'm call - ing, Lit-tle, lit-tle lambs are play-ing,

Pä-kä,[2] pä-kä, pow'r-ful-ly pranc-ing rams, Pä-kä, pä-kä, rams are stray-ing.

Soft-ly the dark-ness veils the land, Lone-ly I long for my lov-er's hand,

Sure-ly to-mor-row we a-gain will be, Safe in the glade by the lov-er's tree.

Tu-ku, tu-ku, tuu I'm call - ing, Lit-tle, lit-tle lambs are play - ing.

Pä-kä, pä-kä, pow'r-ful-ly pranc-ing rams, Pä-kä, pä-kä, rams are stray-ing.

[2]*Pronounce* the ä as the *ai* in "pair."

White Llamas

Translated by Christine Turner Curtis

Peruvian (Quechua Indian) Folk Song

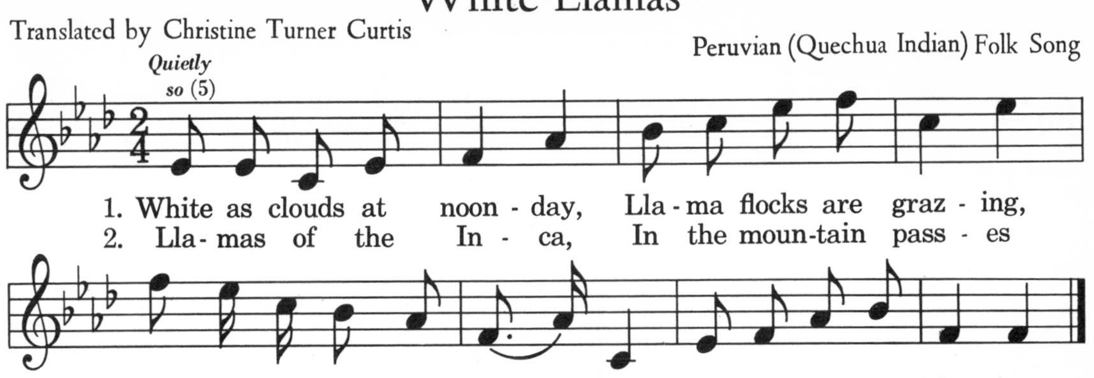
Quietly
so (5)
1. White as clouds at noon-day, Lla-ma flocks are graz-ing,
2. Lla-mas of the In-ca, In the moun-tain pass-es
High in the Cor-dil-le-ra, Where the sun is blaz-ing.
Feed on the fra-grant moun-tain herbs, Eat the flow-'ring grass-es.

Colly, My Cow

Traditional

In the English Folk-Style
by Katherine K. Davis

Playfully
mi la
1. A sto-ry, a sto-ry I'll tell you just now;
2. Says lit-tle Tom Dick-er, "Pray what do you mean
3. Then com-eth the tan-ner with whip at his side.
It's all a-bout sell-ing of Col-ly, my cow!
By sell-ing your Col-ly when she is so lean?"
He bids me three shil-lings for Col-ly, my pride.
CHORUS
Ah, pret-ty Col-ly, pret-ty Col-ly, my cow!
Poor Col-ly will give no more milk to me now!

4. The skin of my Colly
is softer than silk,
And three times a day
does my Colly give milk.

5. Then good-by, dear Colly,
she's gone past recall.
She's sold to a tanner,
her horns, head, and all.

Fola, Fola Blakken[1]
Translated
Edvard Grieg
In a playful mood
do (1)
p
1. Fo - la, fo - la blak - ken! You are ver - y tired I know, You shall have some oats and bran now, Fo - la, fo - la blak - ken. Oh, that steep and
2. Fa - ther took his coat off. Fo - la blak-ken can't do that. You must sweat in your warm hide, You good old fo - la blak - ken. Soon you'll be a -
3. Fo - la, fo - la blak - ken! Go in - to your lit - tle stall. Ver - y soon this boy will come And pat you, fo - la blak - ken. Can't you see me
[1]Pronounce fo-la block-en. A little black pony.

high hill And that long and marsh - y moor, That was ver - y
sleep - ing, No more work for you to - day, No more chaf - ing
smil - ing? Will you like my mes - sage? Fa - ther says that
hard on you, My fo - la, fo - la blak - ken.
from the har-ness, Fo - la, fo - la blak - ken.
you can rest To - mor-row, fo - la blak - ken.
quietly
4. Dream of that, dear blak - ken. You shall on - ly eat and rest,
(Continued on next page.)

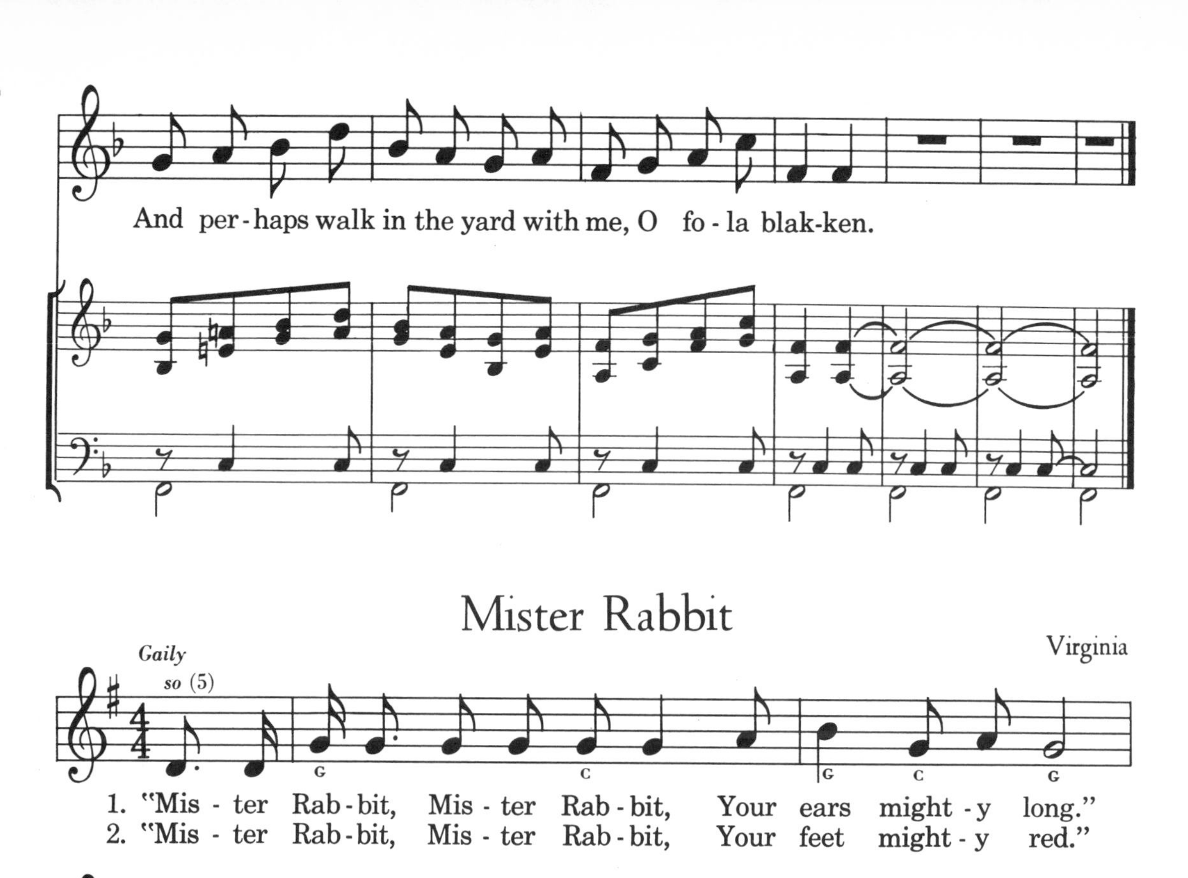
And per-haps walk in the yard with me, O fo-la blak-ken.
Mister Rabbit
Virginia
Gaily
so (5)
1. "Mis-ter Rab-bit, Mis-ter Rab-bit, Your ears might-y long."
2. "Mis-ter Rab-bit, Mis-ter Rab-bit, Your feet might-y red."

"Yes, good sir, they're put on · wrong!" · Ev - 'ry lit-tle soul must
"Yes, good sir, I'm al-most dead." · Ev - 'ry lit-tle soul must

shine, shine, shine, · Ev - 'ry lit-tle soul must shine, shine, shine.
shine, shine, shine, · Ev - 'ry lit-tle soul must shine, shine, shine.

3. "Mister Rabbit, Mister Rabbit,
You're in a mighty habit,
Goin' in my garden, cuttin' down my cabbage."
Ev'ry little soul must shine, shine, shine,
Ev'ry little soul must shine, shine, shine.

4. "Mister Rabbit, Mister Rabbit,
Your tail's mighty white."
"Yes, good sir, and I'm gettin' out of sight."
Ev'ry little soul must shine, shine, shine,
Ev'ry little soul must shine, shine, shine.

Björnstjerne Björnson
Translated

The Fox and the Hare

Halfdan Kjerulf

With steady motion
so (5)
mi (3)
1. There lay a fox un - der - neath a root by the
2. Then hid the fox with a cun - ning guile in the
3. The fox's · heart went a clop - a - clop, in the
heath - er, by the heath - er. A hare came skip-ping on a
heath - er, in the heath - er. The hare came leap-ing with a
heath - er, in the heath - er. "I'll make my din - ner of a
dain - ty foot · through the heath - er, through the heath - er. "Oh,
care-less smile, through the heath - er, through the heath - er. "My
rab - bit chop, · on the heath - er, on the heath - er." But,
a little faster
fi (♮4)
what a glo - ri - ous sum - mer day; The sun-beams too seem to
paws are light as a pair of wings," He said, while mak - ing a
Mis - ter Hare saw a nose of gray. "Good - by, Sir Fox, I must

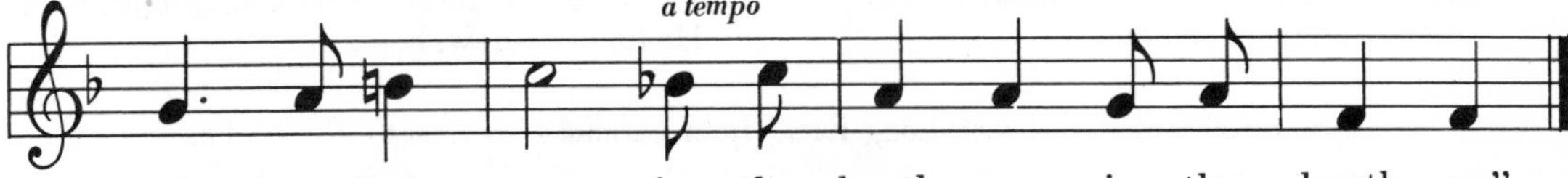
a tempo
skip on their way, in the heath - er, in the heath - er."
cou - ple of springs on the heath - er, on the heath - er.
be on my way, through the heath - er, through the heath - er."

Sweetly Sings the Donkey

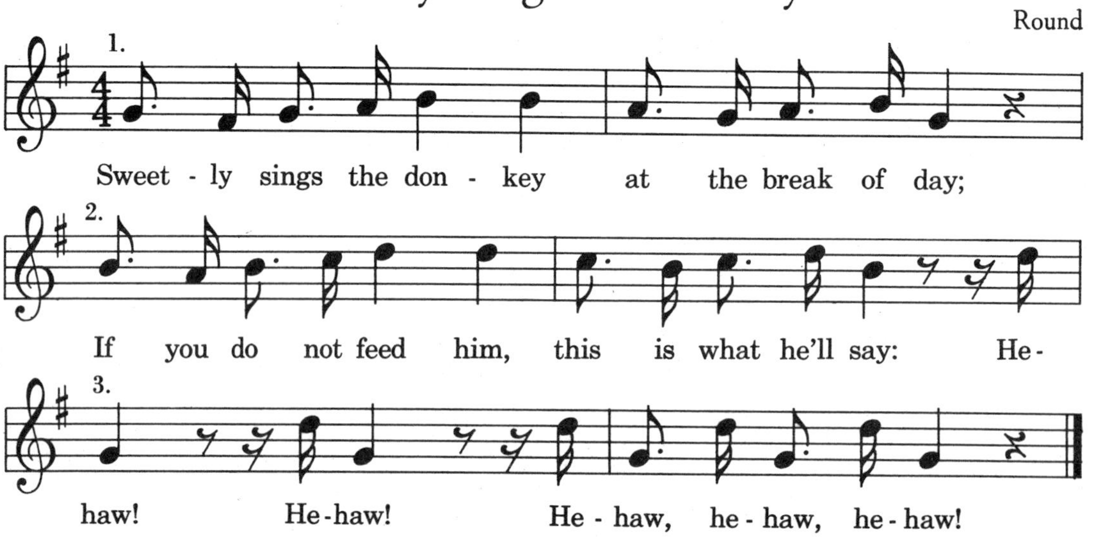
Round
1.
Sweet - ly sings the don - key at the break of day;
2.
If you do not feed him, this is what he'll say: He-
3.
haw! He-haw! He - haw, he - haw, he - haw!

The Last Will and Testament of the Gray Mule

Traditional

Old Tune

Humorously
mi (3)
1. John Cook he had · a lit-tle gray mule; He-haw, he - haw, he - haw!
2. John Cook was rid-ing up Shu - ter's bank; He-haw, he - haw, he - haw!

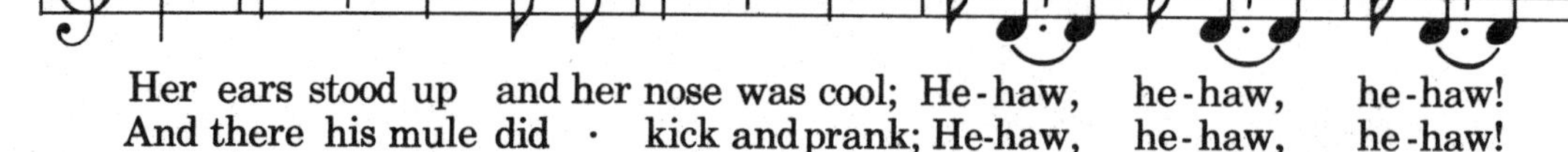
Her ears stood up and her nose was cool; He-haw, he-haw, he-haw!
And there his mule did · kick and prank; He-haw, he-haw, he-haw!

3. John Cook was riding up Shuter's hill;
   He-haw, he-haw, he-haw!
   His mule fell down and she made her will;
   He-haw, he-haw, he-haw!

4. The saddle and bridle were laid on the shelf;
   He-haw, he-haw, he-haw!
   If you want any more you can sing it yourself;
   He-haw, he-haw, he-haw!

Listen to "Personages with Long Ears," from *Carnival of the Animals*, Saint-Saëns. (Victor record.)

Listen to "The Little White Donkey," Ibert. (Decca album "Animal Pictures in Music")

On the Road to Willamolay

L. E. Watters

Spanish Folk Melody[1]

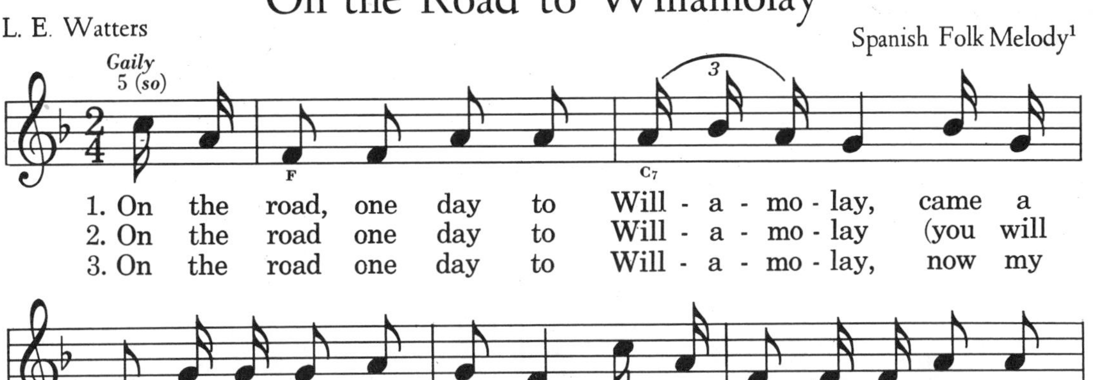
Gaily
5 (so)
3

1. On the road, one day to Will - a - mo - lay, came a
2. On the road one day to Will - a - mo - lay (you will
3. On the road one day to Will - a - mo - lay, now my

mule with a man a - rid - ing. Said the man, "How · far to
doubt what I say, I'm think - ing.) "Do you have an - y hay in
yarn's get - ting long and wid - er; How the mule that · day to

3

Will - a - mo - lay?" as he down from his mule came slid - ing, The
Will - a - mo - lay?" asked the man, his · eye a - wink - ing. The
Will - a - mo - lay ran a - way with - out his rid - er. My

la - zy mule he heard me say, "It is a mile." He
la - zy mule he heard me say, "There's lots of hay." Be -
tale should teach you this: re - mem - ber all your years, Be -

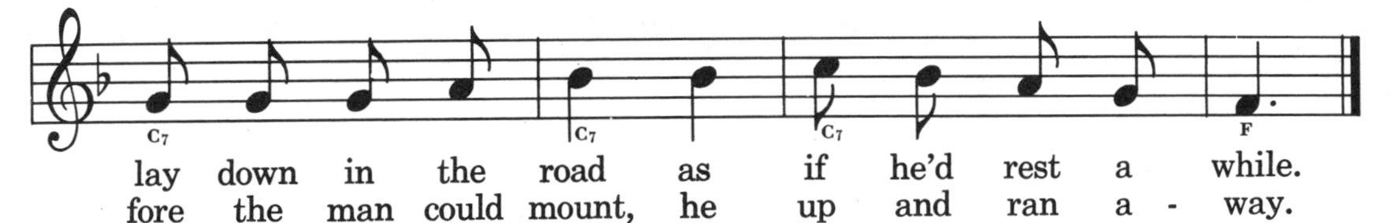

lay down in the road as if he'd rest a while.
fore the man could mount, he up and ran a - way.
fore you tell a se - cret, see who has big ears!

[1]Melody used by permission of G. Schirmer, Inc., copyright owner of *Spanish Songs of Old California*, collected by Charles F. Lummis.

My Donkey Diodoro[1]

English version by John Sumner
Lively
so (5)
mi (3)
Italian Folk Song
1. My don-key is a slow one, He lifts his feet for no one. When whips be-gin their snap-ping It · is his cue for nap - ping.
2. I named him for a schol - ar, Put on his neck a col - lar. In-stead of trot-ting bet - ter He · treats it as a fet - ter.
3. I deck his mane with ros - es, He on - ly blinks and doz-es. In-stead of brisk - ly run - ning, He · spends his time in sun - ning.
CHORUS
Di - o - do - ro, I bought him to my sor - row,
Di - o - do - ro is balk - y as a mule.
F
C7

One of you play this on the piano while the others sing.

[1]*Pronounce* dee oh daw′roh.

ABOUT SINGING THINGS

Bells

Bells in the country,
They sing the heart to rest
When night is on the high road
And day is in the west.

Robert Nathan

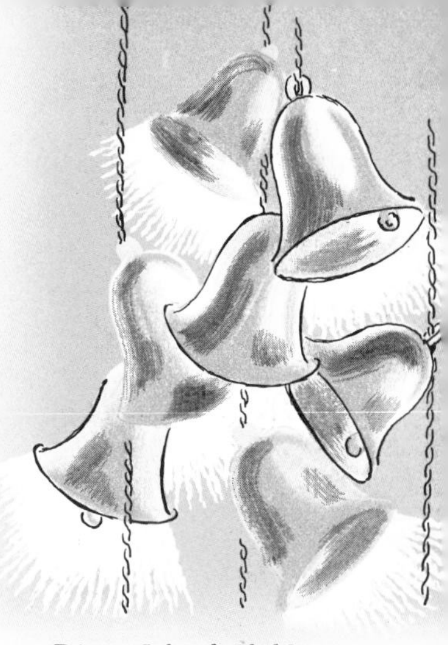

The Bell
English text by Cecil Cowdrey
Puerto Rican School Children
Not too slow
mi (3)
Lit-tle bell, ah, lit-tle com-rade, In your bel-fry near the sky,
Long you're si-lent, ev-er griev-ing, Mourn-ing those who went a-way.
Yet to-day I feel you stir-ring, Bless-ed ti-dings you would tell.
Home re-turn-ing, home re-turn-ing, They are com-ing, lit-tle bell,
Home re-turn-ing, home re-turn-ing, They are com-ing, lit-tle bell.
Swing-ing, ring-ing, ring-ing, swing-ing, Ring out, ring out, sweet bell.

Listen to "The Carillon," from *L'Arlesienne Suite*, Bizet. (Victor or Columbia record.)

Bells Above the Chapel
Ann Bowles
Polish Folk Tune
Slowly
so
mi
1. Hear the bells a - bove the chap - el, Ding, dong, ding, dong,
2. When the bells a bove the chap - el, Ding, dong, ding, dong,
1. Ding, dong, ding, dong, ding, dong, ding, dong! Hear the bells a - bove the chap-el
2. Ding, dong, ding, dong, ding, dong, ding, dong! When the bells a - bove the chap-el
ding, dong, ding, dong! Hear the bells a - bove the chap - el
ding, dong, ding, dong! When the bells a - bove the chap - el
Ring - ing out so peace - ful - ly. Ding, dong, ding, dong,
Chime their mes-sage far and wide. Ding, dong, ding, dong,
Ring - ing out so peace - ful - ly. Ding, dong, ding, dong!
Chime their mes - sage far and wide. Ding, dong, ding, dong!
ding, dong, ding, dong!
ding, dong, ding, dong!
Ding, dong, ding, ding, dong!
Ding, dong, ding, ding, dong!
Ding, dong, ding, dong, Ding, dong, ding - a - ding - a - dong!
Ding, dong, ding, dong, Ding, dong, ding - a - ding - a - dong!

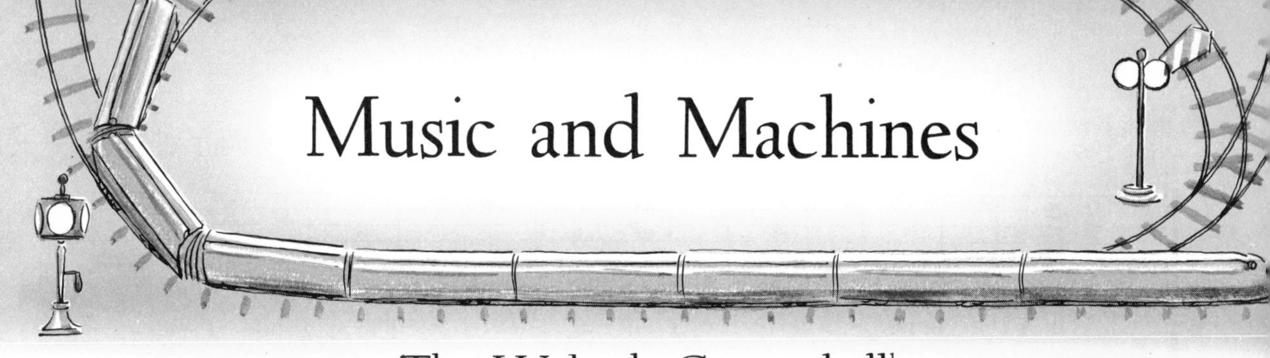

Music and Machines

The Wabash Cannonball[1]

William Kindt

In ballad style

la
G
G
C
C

1. From the great At - lan - tic O - cean to the wide Pa - cif - ic shore,
CHORUS So · lis - ten to the jin - gle, the · jum - ble and the roar

D7
D7
D7
G

To the green old flow-'ring moun-tains, to · ice-bound Lab - ra - dor,
As she glides a - long the wood-lands through the hills and by the shore.

G
G
C
C

She's · long and tall and · hand-some and · known quite well to all,
Hear the might-y rush of the en - gine and the lone-some ho-boes squall,

D7
D7
D7
G

She's the mod-ern com - bi - na - tion called the Wa-bash Can-non - ball.
While · rid-ing through the jun - gle on the Wa-bash Can-non - ball.

2. She came in from Birmingham on a cold and frosty day,
As she rolled into the station you could hear the people say,
There's a gal out there from Tennessee, she's long, boy, and tall,
She's the modern combination called the Wabash Cannonball.

3. Now the eastern states are dandy, so all the people say,
From New York to St. Louis and Chicago by the way,
From the lakes of Minnesota where the rippling waters fall,
No change in standard gauging on the Wabash Cannonball.

[1]Used by permission of the M. M. Cole Publishing Company, Chicago, Ill. Performance rights controlled by B. M. I.

A Bicycle Built for Two

Harry Dacre

In waltz time
so (5)
G G C G
Dai - sy, Dai - sy, Give me your an - swer, do,
D7 G A7 D7
I'm half cra - zy, All for the love of you,
D7 G G C G
It won't be a styl - ish mar - riage! I can't af - ford a car - riage,
G D7 G D7 G D7 G
But you'll look sweet on the seat Of a bi - cy - cle built for two.

We Sing and Play

Listen When the Orchestra Begins

Nancy Byrd Turner

Peter Dalton

Moderately

so (5)

1. The vi - o - lin's a la - dy, · And at her win-dow sings; ·
2. There's some-thing ver - y sol - emn · A - bout the rich bas - soon; ·
3. The trum - pet is a sol - dier, · The trom-bone is an earl; ·

The cel - lo is a trou - ba - dour, His voice is rich and deep; ·
The tu - ba and the Eng - lish horn Are hunt - ers on a hill; ·
The o - boes, hap - py chil-dren, play And call the vi - o - lins; ·

The clar - i - net's a hap - py lad, His mel - low mu - sic rings; ·
The French horn is a wan - der - er A - far be-neath the moon; ·
The pic - co - lo and tim - pa - ni Are laugh-ing boys and girls. ·

The flute's a shep-herd call - ing home, call - ing home his sheep. ·
The harp's a love - ly maid - en, maid - en by a rill. ·
Just lis - ten when the or - ches - tra, or - ches - tra be - gins. ·

Ring, Ring the Banjo!

Stephen C. Foster

Happily
5 (so)
F F F C7
1. The time is nev - er drear-y If a fel - low nev - er groans;
2. Oh! nev - er count the bub-bles While there's wa-ter in the spring.
do (1). . . . . do . . . . do . . . . so (5)
F F C7 F
The la - dies nev - er wea - ry With the rat - tle of the bones.
A fel - low has no trou - bles While he's got this song to sing.
do . . . . do . . . . so . . . . do
F F F C7
Then come a - gain, Su - san - na, By the gas - light of the moon;
The beau - ties of cre - a - tion Will · nev - er lose their charm
do . . . . do . . . . do . . . . so
F F C7 F
We'll · tum the old pi - an - o When the ban - jo's out of tune.
While I roam the old plan - ta - tion With my true love on my arm.
do . . . . do . . . . so . . . . . so . . . . . do
CHORUS
F F F C7
Ring, ring the ban - jo! I like that good old song.
do . . . . do . . . . do . . . . so
F F C7 F
Come a - gain my true love; Oh, where you been so long?
do . . . . do . . . . so . . . . do

Listen to "The Banjo," Gottschalk. (Victor record.)
Listen to "Jazz Pizzicato," Anderson. (Victor record.)

Translated by H. M. H.

Peter, the Fiddler

Norwegian Folk Song

Lively
so (5)
1. Per[1] Spill - man, he had on - ly one lone - ly cow,
2. Per Spill - man played gai - ly on his vi - o - lin,
Per Spill - man, he had on - ly one lone - ly cow.
Per Spill - man played gai - ly on his vi - o - lin.
He trad - ed the cow for an old vi - o - lin,
The mu - sic he fid - dled made ev - 'ry - one dance,
He trad - ed the cow for an old vi - o - lin.
The mu - sic he fid - dled made ev - 'ry - one dance.
"You good old fid - dle,
"You vi - o - lin, you vi - o - lin, you
vi - o - lin, you vi - o - lin, you fid - dle mine."
fid - dle, good old fid - dle mine."

[1] *Pronounce* pear. *Per Spillman means Peter, the Fiddler.*

The Fiddlers' Tune

Violin
Lively
L. E. Watters
Piano
Fine
4
D.C. al Fine

Skip to My Lou
Traditional Singing Game
mi (3)
1. Lost my part-ner, what will I do; Lost my part-ner, what will I do;
Lost my part-ner, what will I do? Skip to my Lou, my dar - ling.
CHORUS
Skip, skip, skip to my Lou; Skip, skip, skip to my Lou;
Skip, skip, skip to my Lou; Skip to my Lou, my dar - ling.

2. I'll get another one, better than you.
3. Can't get a red bird, a blue bird will do.
4. Little red wagon, painted blue.
5. Fly in the sugar bowl, shoo, shoo, shoo.

Orchestration for Skip to My Lou

Arranged by L. E. Watters
Violins, flutes and melody instruments.
B flat Clarinets and B flat saxophones.
E flat Altos (mellophones) and E flat saxophones.
B flat Cornets and trumpets.
Cellos, trombones, and baritones. Tubas should play lower notes.
Drums, cymbals, triangles and sandblocks.
Piano
Auto harp and guitar.
F
C7
F
B♭
C7
F

The Street Band

L. E. W. — L. E. Watters

so (5)
Come join the band, you may play the cor - net,
mi (3)
If you like har - mo - ny,
do (1)
Boom ta ta, boom ta ta, boom ta ta, boom ta ta ta,
Or if you like play clar - i - net.
You may play the horn.
Boom ta ta, boom ta ta, boom ta ta, boom.

Listen to "Semper Fidelis," Sousa. Played by U. S. Marine Band. (Victor record.)

Listen to "March of the Three Kings," from *L'Arlésienne Suite,* Bizet. (Victor Rhythm Album Four.)

The Marching Band

R. C. B.
Richard C. Berg
Quickly
so (5)
C G7 C G7 C G7 C
The band is march-ing down the street, The play-ers all in step;
dm dm D7 G7
The drum-mers keep a stead - y beat, The twirl - ers* add the pep!
C G7 C G7 C G7 C
The in - stru-ments are shin - ing, And the u - ni - forms are neat;
I hope some day that I may play, And nev - er miss a beat
1
Fine
F C dm G7 C
Hear the band a - play-ing As it march-es down the street!
With a band a - play-ing As it march-es down the street!
E7 am E7 am
Ta ta ta ta ta ta ta ta, Ta ta ta ta ta ta!
D.S. al Fine
D7 G D7 G7
Ta ta ta ta ta ta ta ta, Ta ta ta ta ta ta!
Snare drum
Drum part
Bass drum

This song may be used as a two-part ensemble for melody instruments.

*Does anyone in class twirl a baton? If so, let's have them twirl as we play and sing.

The Tootin' Turk

L. E. Watters

Richard C. Berg

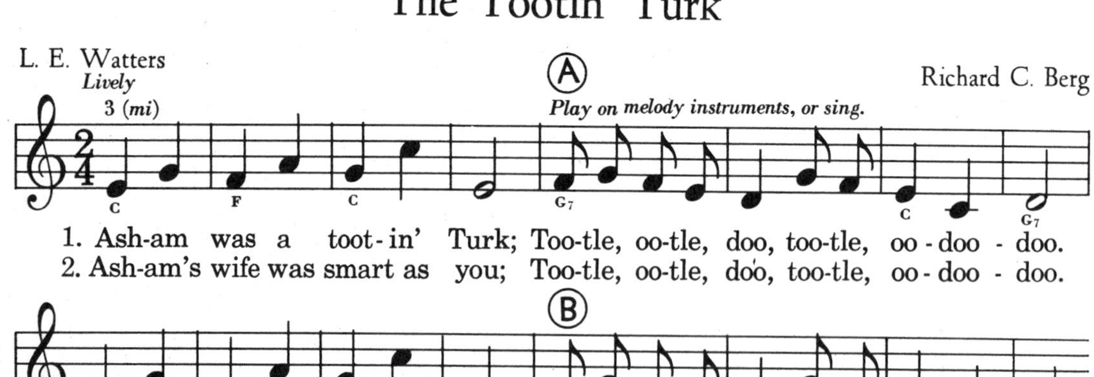

Lively
3 (mi)
A
Play on melody instruments, or sing.
B
C F C G7 C G7
C F C G7 C

1. Ash-am was a toot-in' Turk; Too-tle, oo-tle, doo, too-tle, oo-doo-doo.
2. Ash-am's wife was smart as you; Too-tle, oo-tle, doo, too-tle, oo-doo-doo.

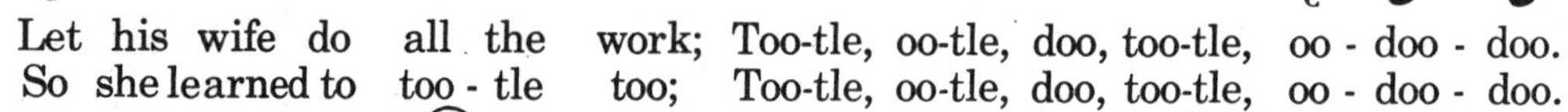

Let his wife do all the work; Too-tle, oo-tle, doo, too-tle, oo-doo-doo.
So she learned to too-tle too; Too-tle, oo-tle, doo, too-tle, oo-doo-doo.

C
D
F C

He played a-way, too-tle, oo-tle, oo-doo, Ev-'ry day, too-tle, oo-tle, oo-doo.
She played a-way, too-tle, oo-tle, oo-doo, Ev-'ry day, too-tle, oo-tle, oo-doo.

E
C F C G7 C

Ash-am was a toot-in' Turk; Too-tle, oo-tle, doo, too-tle, oo-doo-doo.
Ash-am's wife was smart as you; Too-tle, oo-tle, doo, too-tle, oo-doo-doo.

3. Any day duets you hear; Tootle, ootle, doo, tootle, oo-doo-doo.
Asham and his wifey dear; Tootle, ootle, doo, tootle, oo-doo-doo.
They play away, tootle, ootle, oo-doo, Every day, tootle, ootle, oo-doo.
Any day duets you hear; Tootle, ootle, doo, tootle, oo-doo-doo.

4. Now his task he doesn't shirk; Tootle, ootle, doo, tootle, oo-doo-doo.
Helps his wife do all the work; Tootle, ootle, doo, tootle, oo-doo-doo.
They play away, tootle, ootle, oo-doo, Every day, tootle, ootle, oo-doo.
Now his task he doesn't shirk; Tootle, ootle, doo, tootle, oo-doo-doo.

5. It's the truth that tootin's fun; Tootle, ootle, doo, tootle, oo-doo-doo.
When your daily work is done; Tootle, ootle, doo, tootle, oo-doo-doo.
So play away, tootle, ootle, oo-doo, Every day, tootle, ootle, oo-doo.
Asham was a tootin' Turk; Tootle, ootle, doo, tootle, oo-doo-doo.

"Tootle too" part for flutes.
A
B
C
D
E
"Tootle too" part for B flat clarinets.
A
B
C
D
E

The Royal Trumpeter

In march time
L. E. Watters
5 (so)
1. There once was a trum - pet - er, a loy - al sub - ject he,
2. He came to the pal - ace and he climbed up - on the wall
3. Right up to the throne he marched with proud and state - ly tread,
Who told his friends, "I hope some day to play for roy - al - ty."
To be the first to see the Prince, and play the sig - nal call.
He saw them place the jew - eled crown up - on the Princ - e's head.
And then one day he heard that soon the Prince would wear the crown.
He saw the great pro - ces - sion and he heard the peo - ple shout;
"All hail our Roy - al Maj - es - ty," he heard the peo - ple sing;
He pol - ished well his trum-pet and set off for Lon - don Town.
He lift - ed up his trum-pet and its mel - o - dy rang out.
He raised his shin - ing trum-pet and he played it for the King.
Ta ta ta ta, ta ta ta ta, Ta ta ta ta ta, ta ta ta ta.
Parts for trumpets.

Listen to "Grand March," from *Aida*, Verdi. (Victor Rhythm Album Four.)

SHINING HOURS

Hansel and Gretel

Adapted from the Opera of Engelbert Humperdinck and Adelheid Wette

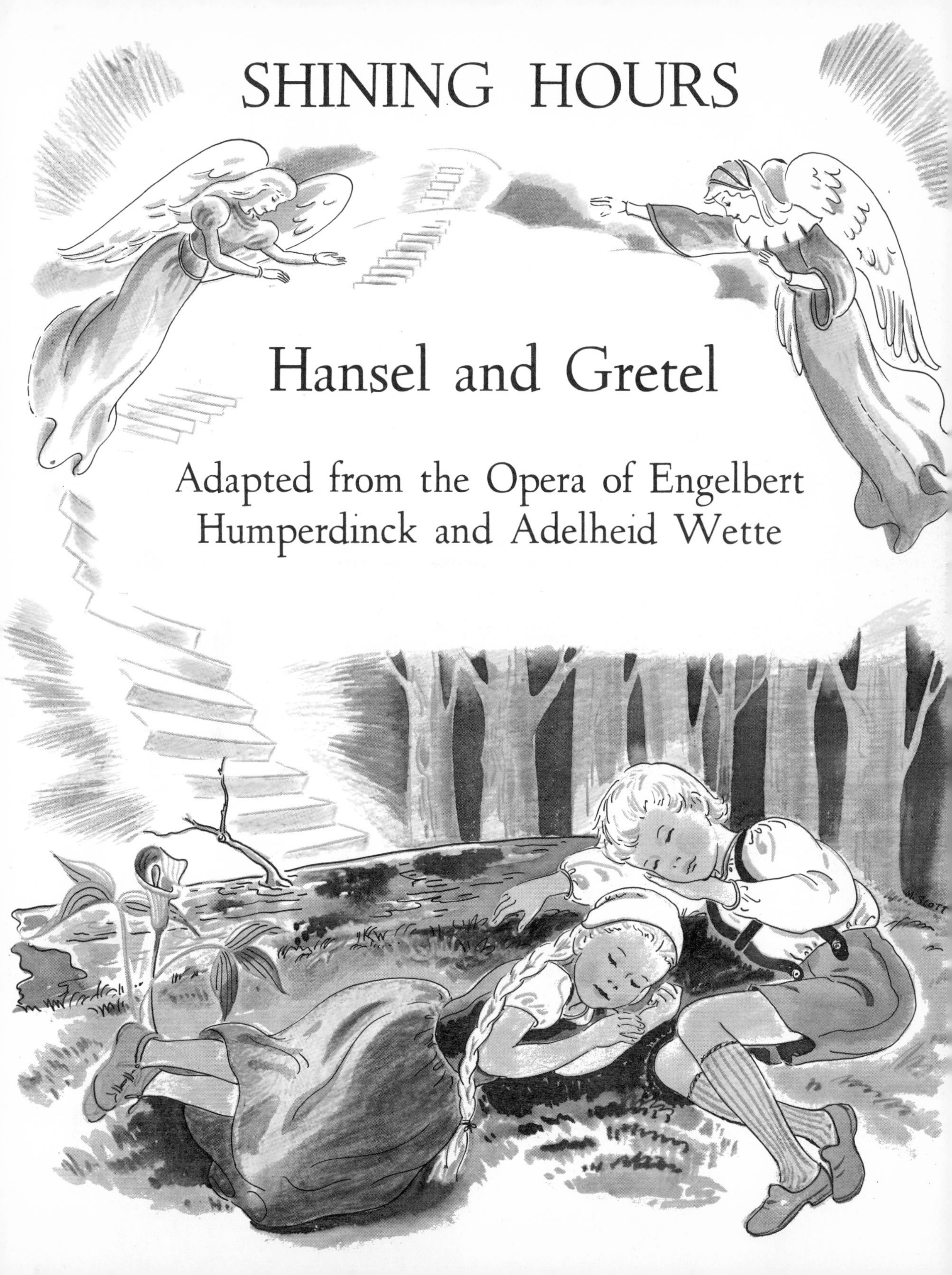
M. SCOTT

OVERTURE

Arranged and adapted for small orchestra by L. E. Watters
Violins
A
B
C
B flat Cornets and trumpets
A
7
B
C

B flat Clarinets
A
B
C

E flat Altos (mellophones) and E flat Saxophones. (Saxophones play an octave higher than written.)
A
7
B
C

Cello, trombone and baritone.
A
B
C
Drums
roll
A
B
triangle
2
C
cymbal

The piano part for this overture is in your teacher's book.

The Story of "Hansel and Gretel"

AT HOME

Hansel and Gretel were the children of Peter, a poor broom-maker, and Gertrude, his wife. They lived in a simple thatched cottage.

One day Peter went to the village to sell his brooms. While he was gone his wife went to the field to gather bunches of grass to make more brooms. Before they left, the father said, "Hansel, work on this broom I have started. Have it finished when I get back." The mother said, "Gretel, my dear, please be busy with knitting this stocking while I am gone. I hope it will be several inches longer when I get back."

Hansel and Gretel worked for a while, but soon they became tired. Also they became hungry. There was no food in the house. Gretel said, "Hansel, let's sing a song. Then we will forget how hungry we are." So they sang:

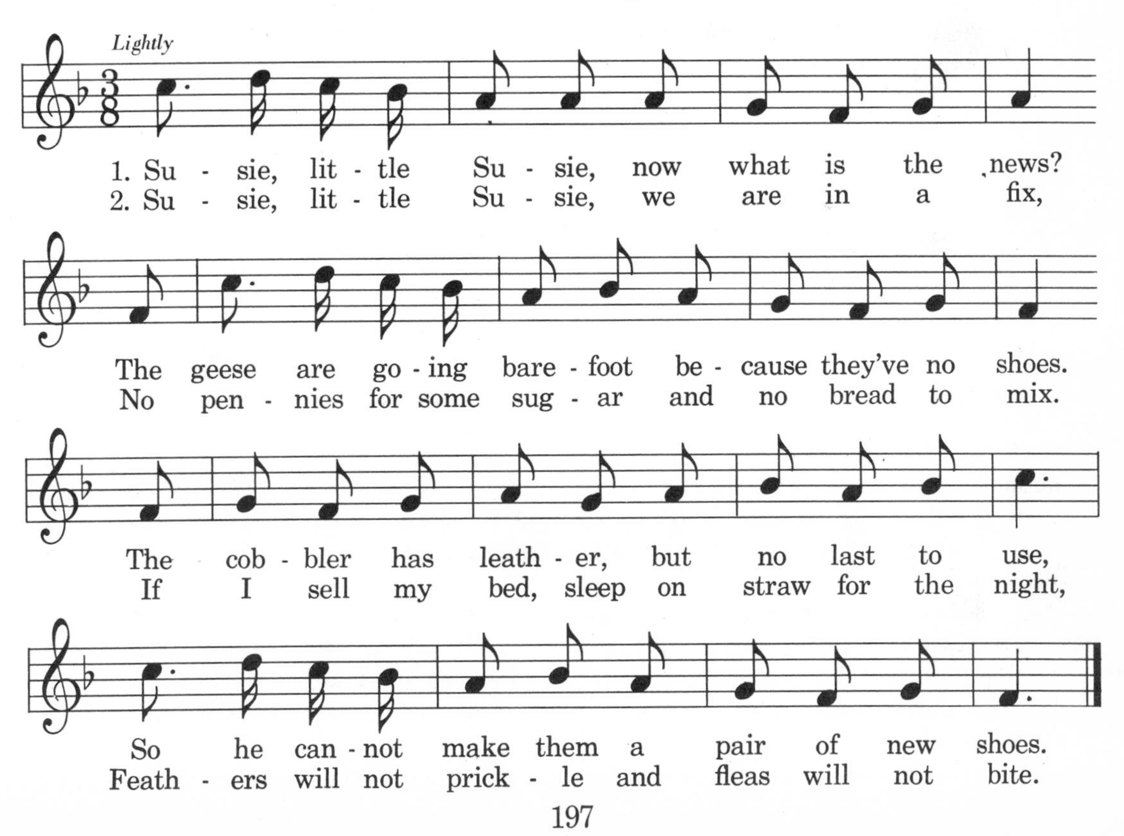
Lightly
1. Su - sie, lit - tle Su - sie, now what is the news?
2. Su - sie, lit - tle Su - sie, we are in a fix,
The geese are go - ing bare - foot be - cause they've no shoes.
No pen - nies for some sug - ar and no bread to mix.
The cob - bler has leath - er, but no last to use,
If I sell my bed, sleep on straw for the night,
So he can - not make them a pair of new shoes.
Feath - ers will not prick - le and fleas will not bite.

But after they sang their song they were still hungry. Hansel said, "For weeks we have eaten nothing but bread. What a treat it would be to have some eggs and butter to eat."

"Hush," said Gretel. "Don't you remember what father said when mother was sad?"

When our grief we can-not bear, God, the Lord, will hear · our pray'r.

"It's all right for you to say that," said Hansel, "but I'm hungry! I still wish we had some butter and—"

"Oh, don't be a crosspatch," interrupted Gretel. "I'm just as hungry as you are. Let's get back to our work."

They started to work again, but soon Hansel was grumbling. Gretel said, "If you'll stop complaining I'll tell you a nice secret."

"Good," said Hansel. "I like secrets."

"Look in this jug," said Gretel. "Here is some milk that one of our neighbors sent us. When mother comes home she will make a custard pie for us."

"Oh, jiminy," said Hansel, "a custard pie! Yummy! How thick is the cream?" He put his finger in the cream, and then to his mouth.

"Stop that," said Gretel. "Go back to your work."

"I don't want to work," said Hansel. "Dancing is a lot more fun."

"Oh yes, Hansel. Let's dance awhile. It will help us to work all the faster. Let's dance to a song that auntie used to sing to us."

GRETEL
Quite lively
Broth - er, come and dance with me, Both my hands I give to thee;
Right foot first, left foot then, Round a - bout and back a - gain.
HANSEL
I would dance, but don't know how, When to step and when to bow;
Show me what I ought to do And then I'll come and dance with you.
BOTH
Let your feet go tap, tap, tap, Let your hands go clap, clap, clap;
Let your head go nick, nick, nick, Let your fin - gers click, click, click;
Right foot first, left foot then, Round a - bout and back a - gain.
Right foot first, left foot then, Round a - bout and back a - gain.

Round and round the room they danced. At first Hansel was clumsy, but Gretel taught him to dance the steps gracefully. They whirled around and around, laughing and singing, forgetting their work and their hunger. They danced faster and faster, until they lost their balance and tumbled over one another onto the floor. Just then the door opened and their mother walked into the room.

"What's all this rumpus about?" said their mother, as she set her bundle of broom-grass down on the floor. "Gretel, you haven't finished your stocking, and you, Hansel, haven't finished a single broom. I'll fetch my stick, you lazybones, and make your fingers tingle."

As she turned around she bumped into the jug of milk, and it fell to the floor.

"There goes our supper. Now what are we going to eat?" She took a basket from the wall and thrust it into Gretel's hand. "Go to the woods, you two, and don't you dare to come back until the basket is full of strawberries."

After the children had gone she sat down by the table and wept because she had no food for her family. She was very tired and soon she fell asleep.

PETER'S RETURN

Soon afterward the jolly voice of Peter was heard from a distance, singing this song:

Heartily
Tra la la la, tra la la la, Lit - tle moth-er, here am I, Tra la la la, tra la la la, Bring-ing luck and jol - li - ty.
Tra la la la, tra la la la, There's a big hole in my purse, Tra la la la, tra la la la, In the stom-ach it is worse.
Tra la la la, tra la la la, Life for some of us is rough, Tra la la la, tra la la la, Hun-ger is a fight - er tough.

Peter came through the door carrying a big basket filled with all kinds of good things to eat. He set the basket on the table and aroused his wife, shouting joyfully, "Gertrude, see what I have brought home!"

She looked at the basket with amazement and said, "What do I see? Ham, butter, a dozen eggs, turnips, onions, and some tea! They must have cost a fortune!"

"I had such good luck selling brooms for high prices that I couldn't resist buying all this good food." He was so happy that he grabbed his wife and together they danced around and around the room while Peter sang his song over again. When they stopped dancing he said, "Where are Hansel and Gretel?"

Then Gertrude told Peter how idle the children had been and how they had caused her to upset the milk and break the jug.

Peter banged his fist on the table and said, "So those little scalawags have been into mischief again!" Then he became worried. "But it is almost dark. Where can they be?"

"I sent them out to the woods to pick strawberries," answered his wife.

Peter looked startled and said, "Pick strawberries? In the woods? Now they are alone in the gloomy forest, without a moon or stars to light the way. And you know that witch woman lives in the forest. She may catch and eat our children."

Poor Gertrude became so terrified that she rushed out of the house, calling for the children. Peter rushed after her to help find their loved ones.

NIGHT IN THE FOREST

When the children left the house they wandered far into the forest. Hansel found many strawberries, and his basket was full by sundown. Gretel was sitting under a tree, weaving a garland of wild flowers. A jack-in-the-pulpit was growing beside her. She sang this song as she wove:

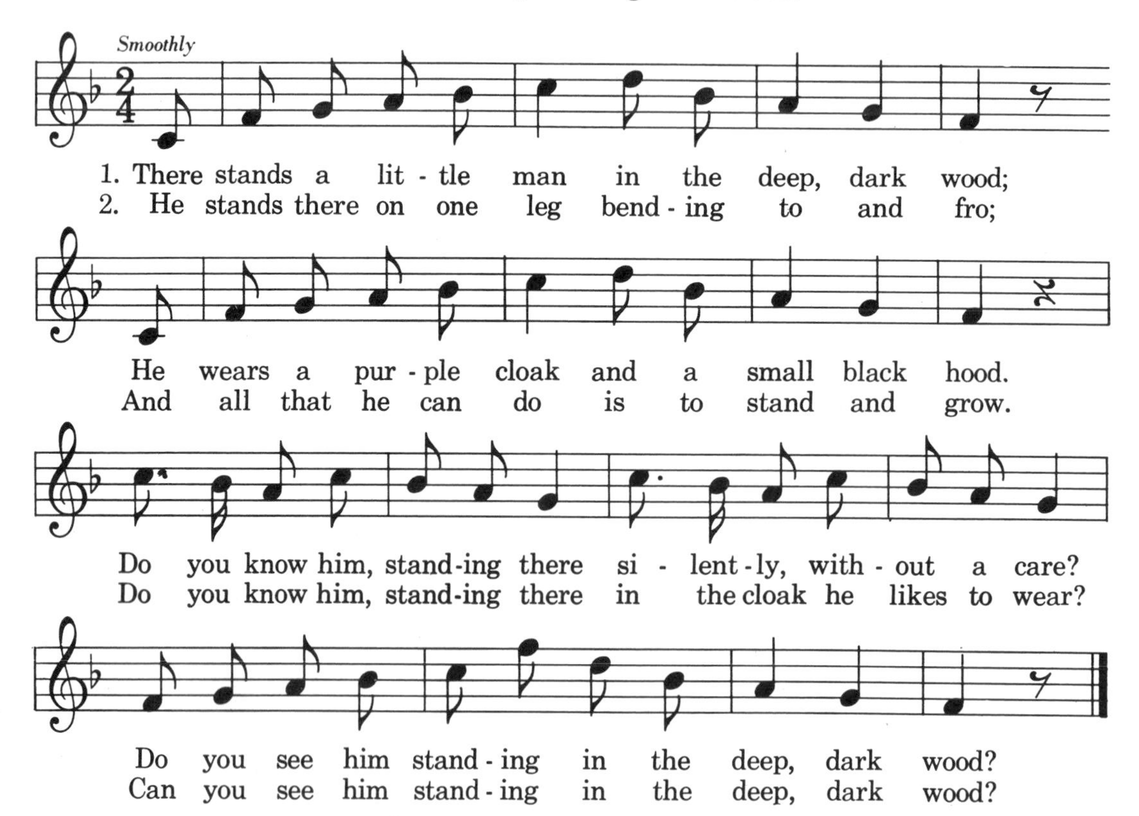
Smoothly
1. There stands a lit - tle man in the deep, dark wood;
2. He stands there on one leg bend - ing to and fro;
He wears a pur - ple cloak and a small black hood.
And all that he can do is to stand and grow.
Do you know him, stand-ing there si - lent-ly, with - out a care?
Do you know him, stand-ing there in the cloak he likes to wear?
Do you see him stand - ing in the deep, dark wood?
Can you see him stand - ing in the deep, dark wood?

Hansel walked over to her, swinging his basket joyfully. "Hurrah! My basket is full to the brim. Mother will be very much pleased."

"My garland is ready also," said Gretel, as she tried to put it on Hansel's head.

"No boy wants to wear one of those," said Hansel. He snatched the garland and put it on Gretel's head. He bowed before her and said, "Now you are the queen of the woods. Here are the strawberries, O queen, but do not eat them all."

Dusk had fallen and the cuckoo was heard. Hansel and Gretel imitated it.

Cuck-oo, cuck-oo, where are you? Cuck-oo, cuck-oo, how are you?

As they continued to imitate the cuckoo they absent-mindedly ate strawberries from the basket. When the bird flew away they were horrified to discover that they had eaten all the berries.

"O heavens!" exclaimed Gretel. "What will mother say?"

"Come now, don't make such a fuss," replied Hansel. "We'll hurry and pick some more."

"But it's too dark to find them," cried Gretel. "Why were we such disobedient children? We should have gone home sooner. I'm afraid!"

"Oh shucks, don't be afraid. Let's hurry home." Hansel looked around uneasily. Then he said, "Gretel, I cannot find the way. But don't lose heart. I'll give a loud call."

He cupped his hands to his mouth and called loudly; but the only answer he got was an echo and a distant call of the cuckoo. He was very tired and frightened, but he didn't want Gretel to know it. He sat down on a log and drew his sister beside him. "Don't be afraid, Gretel. I will take care of you until father finds us." Gretel was terrified by all the sounds she heard and the shadows she saw in the deep, dark woods.

Just then a little gray man with a little gray sack on his back came from behind the trees. "Who are you?" said Gretel as the stranger came toward them. The little man began to sing:

Abridged

Quietly

I shut the chil-dren's peep-ers, *Sh!* And guard the lit - tle sleep-ers, *Sh!*

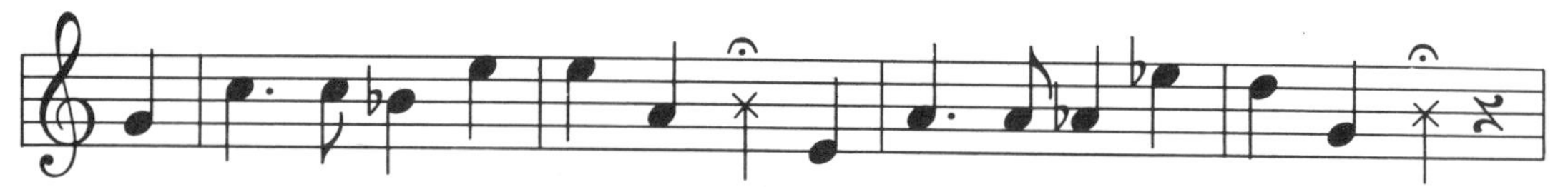

For dear - ly do I love them, *Sh!* And glad - ly watch a - bove them, *Sh!*

not too slow

By ev - 'ry lit - tle child I stand And toss o - ver him some grains of sand,
And if they're good and go to sleep, Then an - gels will come their watch to keep,

And then all the drow - sy eye - lids close In sweet re - pose.
And send ev - 'ry child a hap - py dream In sleep se - rene.

While he was singing, the little man sprinkled sand over the children. When he had gone away they knelt on the ground, folded their hands, and sang their evening prayer.

Solemnly
When at night I go to sleep, · Four-teen an-gels watch do · keep;
Two my head are guard-ing, Two my feet are guid - ing,
Two are on my right hand, · Two are on my left hand,
Two are on my right hand, Two are on my·
Two who warm-ly cov - er, Two who warm-ly hov - er,
left hand, Two who warm-ly cov - er, Two who warm-ly
Two to whom 'tis giv - en To guide my steps to Heav - en.
hov - er, Two to whom 'tis giv'n To guide my steps to Heav'n.

When the children had finished their prayer they sank down on the mossy ground, cuddled close to each other, and fell asleep.

What a beautiful dream they had! The evening mist lifted, and down from the sky on a golden staircase came fourteen angels, dressed in light, floating garments. As they came they hummed beautiful sleep music. They placed themselves in the order mentioned in the song. There they remained until dawn, to protect the children from any harm that might befall them.

THE WITCH'S HOUSE

The morning light came gradually. A Dew Fairy appeared, carrying a flower that was filled with dew. He tripped lightly over to the sleeping children. As he sang he shook the flower, and the dewdrops fell on the children's faces.

Abridged

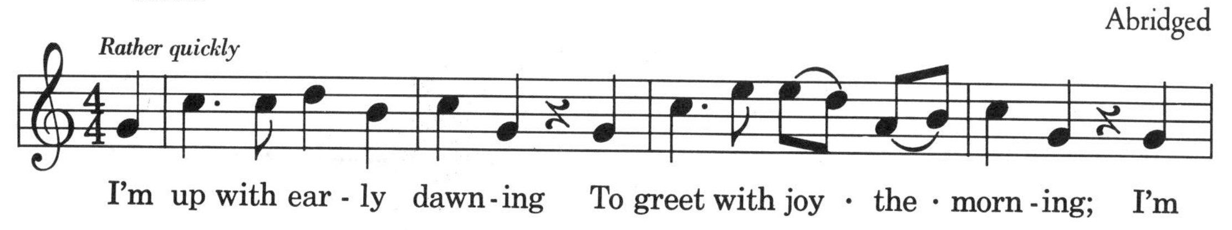

Rather quickly
I'm up with ear - ly dawn - ing To greet with joy · the · morn - ing; I'm

fresh · as a dai - sy, But here are two who are la - zy. Ding,

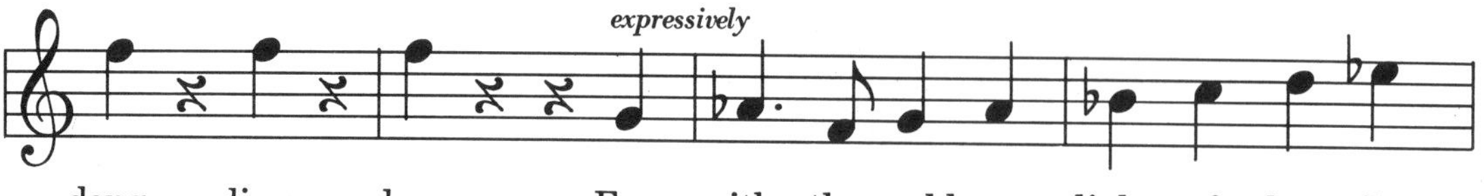

expressively
dong, ding, dong, For with the gold - en light of day I

chase the fad - ing night a - way, Fresh · dew a - round me

shak - ing. It's time all sleep - y heads are wak - ing.

The Dew Fairy skipped away just as Gretel awoke. She rubbed her sleepy eyes and sat up. Birds were singing in the treetops, and Gretel imitated them. She turned to Hansel. "Wake up, you sleepyhead," she said. Then she shook him gently and sang:

Ti - ra li - ra li, it's get - ting late.

Hansel jumped up with a start. He crowed like a rooster and said, "Never have I slept so well! And I had a wonderful dream."

"I had a wonderful dream too," said Gretel. "Fourteen angels came tripping down a golden staircase from heaven, and—"

Hansel interrupted her. "Why, that's the same dream I had."

Just then the morning mist lifted and Hansel turned around. Instead of seeing trees he spied a little house. He stared at it with astonishment. Gretel, seeing the expression on his face, looked in the same direction.

"O Hansel!" she cried, "what do I see? Isn't it a little house?"

"Yes, it is," answered Hansel, "but I have never before seen one like it."

"No wonder," said Gretel. "It is made of gingerbread and cake. And look, it is decorated with raisins and chocolate cream!" They were so delighted that they sang as they walked up to the house.

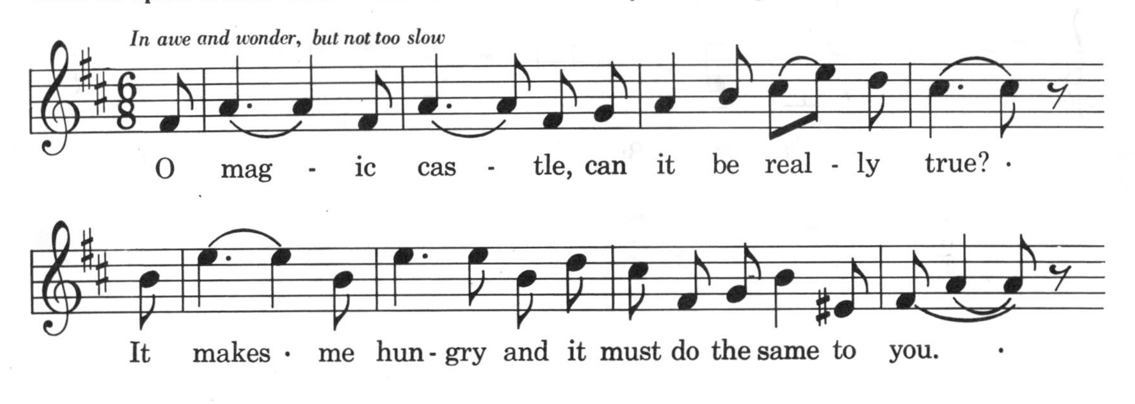

In awe and wonder, but not too slow
O mag - ic cas - tle, can it be real - ly true?
It makes me hun - gry and it must do the same to you.

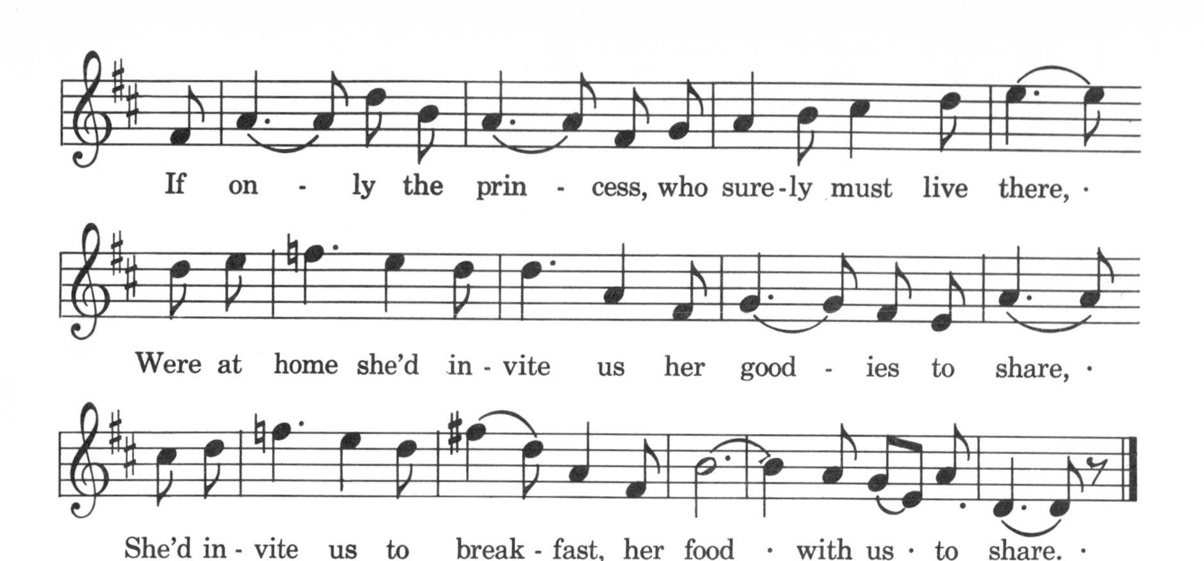
If on - ly the prin - cess, who sure-ly must live there,
Were at home she'd in - vite us her good - ies to share,
She'd in - vite us to break - fast, her food with us to share.

"I can't hear a sound," said Hansel. "Let's go inside."

"Oh no!" said his sister as she held him. "Who knows but that the witch-of-the-woods lives here!"

"Shucks," Hansel replied. "No witch could live in such a lovely house. Anyway, let's eat some of it. I'm hungry!"

He reached out and barely touched the house. Crumbs fell into his hand. "Oh," cried Hansel, "how good they taste." Eagerly they each broke off a large piece and began to eat. When they were through eating them, they reached for more.

Suddenly they heard coming from the house:

Nib-ble, nib-ble! Mous - ie, whose nib-bling at my hous - ie?

"Did you hear? What was that?" said Hansel.

"Oh, it's only the wind," his sister replied. "Let's eat some more." They broke off big pieces and ate them hungrily. They were so busy eating that they did not see the ugly old witch who came out of the house. She crept up behind them until she was close. Then she threw a rope around Hansel and seized Gretel by the arm.

"Who are you?" cried both the children.

"Hee, hee, hee!" laughed the old witch, "I am Rosina Dainty-one. I love all people, especially tender little children. They are so good to eat!"

Terrified, the children struggled to run away, but the old witch held them fast. She pinched Hansel's arm. "Ah, you are too skinny. I'll give you good things to eat. They will fatten you."

In the meantime Hansel got out of the rope. He took Gretel by the hand and they pulled themselves free from the old witch and started to run. But they didn't get far, because they couldn't move a step when the old witch raised her wand and sang:

Ho-cus-po-cus, witch-es' charm!
Move not as you fear my arm!
Back or for-ward do not try,
Fixed you are by e - vil eye!

The old witch led Hansel to a big cage in the yard. She thrust him into it and latched the door. Then she waved her wand over Gretel, so that Gretel could move about. She commanded Gretel to go into the house and get some food for Hansel.

Poor Gretel had to obey. The witch knew she wouldn't run away and leave Hansel. When she came out with the food the witch began to stuff it into Hansel's mouth. Gretel got behind her and waved the witch's wand toward Hansel, saying softly, "Hocus pocus, witch's tree, stiffened body now is free." Now Hansel could move about, but he didn't let the witch know it.

When the witch had stuffed Hansel full of good food she was so delighted with the thought he was getting fat that she took her broomstick and rode gaily around the yard on it. Then she went to the oven to stir up the roaring fire. While she was busy Hansel slipped out of the cage. The witch had decided to eat Gretel first, and called to her, "Come here, my dear. Look into the oven and see all the goodies that I am baking."

Hansel called softly, "Sister dear, be careful."

"Come, my dear Gretel," said the witch, "stand on tiptoe and put your head in the oven."

Gretel pretended to be very stupid, and said, "I'm such a goose. Show me how to do it."

The witch opened the oven door, stood on tiptoe, and leaned forward to show Gretel how to peep into the oven. "This is how you do it"—but just as she said that Hansel and Gretel gave a mighty push, and the old witch toppled over into the oven. Quickly they shut the heavy door and said, "Now, old witch, you will see how it feels to be done to a T."

Hansel and Gretel clasped hands and danced around, merrily chanting, "Hurrah! Hurrah! The witch is dead!"

Suddenly there was a loud noise. It became very dark. Soon the light returned, and Hansel and Gretel found themselves standing among a large group of children. "Look," cried Hansel and Gretel, "all of the cookies and cakes have come to life!" The children sang:

Quietly
We are free, we are free, For - ev - er shall it be.

Gretel said, "But your eyes are closed. You are sleeping, yet you are singing."

Quietly
Touch · us, we · pray That we may all a - wake.

Hansel said, "You touch one, Gretel. I'm afraid to try."

"Yes," said Gretel, "I'll touch this dear little face." She touched the nearest child, who opened his eyes and smiled.

Quietly
Oh, touch us too, Oh, touch us too That we · al - so may a - wake.

Gretel touched all the children, who opened their eyes and smiled, without moving. Then Hansel seized the witch's wand, waved it toward the children, and said, "Hocus pocus, witch's tree, stiffened body now is free."

The happy cookie children jumped up and formed a ring around Hansel and Gretel. They danced around and sang:

Gaily
The · witch is · gone and · we · are · free, We'll sing and dance and
shout with glee; Come, chil - dren all, and · join our ring, We'll
all clasp hands to - geth - er while we sing. So · dance and · sing for there's
food e - nough to eat, So · dance and · sing and ·
soon we'll have a treat While all a - round our joy re-sounds. Through
trees, on the breeze, Our song will float a - long. ·

When the song was ended all the children were surprised to hear a strange echo come back to them. It wasn't an echo at all! It was Hansel's and Gretel's father singing: "Tra la la la, tra la la la, we have looked both far and near; tra la la la, tra la la la, were our children only here."

Peter's voice came nearer and nearer, until suddenly he and his wife came upon the children. "Father! Mother!" shouted Hansel and Gretel as they rushed into the arms of their happy parents. When Peter and Gertrude found that Hansel and Gretel were safe and sound they were delighted. And when they saw that the witch was now a big gingerbread cake and that all the children were free, they were overjoyed.

Peter said, "Look, children, the witch has been caught in her own snare. When our need is greatest the Lord stretches out His hand to us."

Then they all sang:

Solemnly
p
mf
ff
When our grief we can-not bear, · God, the Lord, will hear · our pray'r.

ALPHABETICAL INDEX

[Titles in italics indicate instrumental selections.]

Ain't Gonna Rain, 24
All around the Shu-round, 29
America, 126
Angels in Our Fields, The, 121
Animal Fair, The, 23
Arithmetic Song, 26
As I Went Walking down the Street, 49
At the Spinning Wheel, 51
Autumn Is a Painter, 152
Ballit of the Boll Weevil, The, 54
Bell, The, 178
Bells above the Chapel, 179
Bezem, De (The Broom), 69
Bicycle Built for Two, A, 181
Billy Boy, 95
Blacksmith, The, 66
Blacksmith Sings Merrily, The, 67
Blessed Are the Pure in Heart, 90
Bluebonnets, 163
Boat, a Boat to Cross the Ferry, A, 147
Bold Soldier, The, 38
Brave Knight, The, 39
But the Lord Is Mindful of His Own, 88
Buy My Flowers, 68
Cape Cod Chantey, 64
Captain Jinks, 35
Carol of the Grasses, 116
Chinese Evening Song, 141
Christmas Bells, 112
Christmas Lullaby, 115
Cindy, 92
Coffee Grows on White Oak Trees, 30
Colly, My Cow, 169
Come, My Dove, 41
Come, Thou Almighty King, 12
Come, Ye Maidens, 147
Come, Ye Thankful People, Come, 110
Cowboy's Life, The, 60
Cradle Song, 78
Czech Walking Song, 19
Deep in the Forest, 140
Dixie, 128
Don't Let Your Watch Run Down, 63
Drill, Ye Tarriers, 52
Eating Goober Peas, 61
Erie Canal, The, 62
Evensong, 140
Faith of Our Fathers, 86
Fiddlers' Tune, The, 185
Fisher Maiden, The, 42
Fishermen's Evening Song, 65
Flicka, Will You Dance with Me? 40
Fola, Fola Blakken, 170
Fox and the Hare, The, 173
Frog Went a-Courtin', 8
Give Us the Wintertime, 156
Goin' to Leave Ol'-Texas, 58
Goin' to Ride up in the Chariot, 84
Golden Cage Was Hanging, A, 165
Golden Slumbers Kiss Your Eyes, 14
Good-by, 146
Good Night, 81
Good Night to You All, 81
Halloween Visitor, 107
Hansel and Gretel, 193
Hark! the Herald Angels Sing, 118
Harvest Fun, 150
He Shall Feed His Flock, 104
Hear Our Prayer, O Lord, 89
Holy Spirit, Gift Divine, 85
Home, Sweet Home, 12
How Brightly Shines the Morning Star, 82
Hundred Years Ago, A, 64
Hush-a-by, Baby, 73
I Heard It in the Valley, 158
I Wonder When I Shall Be Married, 50
I'm a Roving Cowboy, 56
In the Plaza, 46
Indian Summer, 153
Jacob's Ladder, 83
Jesu, Joy of Man's Desiring, 98
Kookaburra, 164
Largo from "Xerxes," 105
Last Will and Testament of the Gray Mule, 174
'Leven-Cent Cotton and Forty-Cent Meat, 55
Lightly Row, 148
Lily Princess, The, 162
Listen When the Orchestra Begins, 182
Little Star, 142
'Liza Jane, 10
Lone Dog, 166
Lorita, 166
Lullaby on Christmas Eve, 117
Lullaby and Good Night, 77
Man in the Moon, The, 28
Marching Band, The, 189
Marines' Hymn, The, 129
Mariquita, 45
May Day Carol, 162
Melody from the Opera "Rinaldo," 106
Memories, 71
Minuet in G Major, 100

Minuet in G Minor, 101
Mister Rabbit, 172
Mistress Shady, 93
Moon and Her Children, 143
Morning Is Bright, The, 137
Morning Is Come, 137
Music of the River, 149
My Donkey Diodoro, 176
My Heart Ever Faithful, 97
My Home's in Montana, 9
New Created World, A, 131
Nightingale in the Wood, 165
Nile Boatman's Song, 66
Now Come On, 18
Now Thank We All Our God, 108
O Canada! 130
O Little Town of Bethlehem, 114
O Mary, 116
Oh! Susanna, 7
Old Folks at Home, 70
Old Gaelic Lullaby, 73
On the Road to Willamolay, 175
On a Winter Morning, 122
One More River, 25
Our Heavenly Father, Source of Love, 89
Past Three o'Clock, 69
Pay with a Smile, 44
Peacefully, My Baby, Sleep, 72
Peter, the Fiddler, 184
Peter Piper, 24
Pietro's Hat, 94
Planets, The, 142
Praise to the Living God, 90
Praise to the Lord, 88
Pray God Bless, 112
Prayer of Thanksgiving, 109
Put Your Little Foot, 31
Railroad Corral, The, 57
Rig-a-Jig-Jig, 13
Ring, Ring the Banjo! 183
Round the Campfire, 60
Royal Trumpeter, The, 192
Sepp Has a Little Hen, 167
Shepherds and the Star, 114
Shoo Fly, 32
Signs of Winter, 155
Silent Night, 113
Sing Together, 17
Skaters, The, 154
Skip to My Lou, 186
Sleep, My Bonny, Blue-eyed Little Treasure, 76
Sleep, Sleep, My Darling, 79
Sleighride, The, 157
Slumber, 74
Slumber, Slumber, 80
Smiles, Just like the Sunshine, 16
Song of the Breezes, 145
Song of the Cowboy, A, 59
Song of the Cuckoo, 161
Song on a Hilltop, 144
Sourwood Mountain, 50
Spring Has Come, 159
Spring Song, 160
Star-Spangled Banner, The, 124
Stodola Pumpa, 21
Street Band, The, 188
Such Joy, 19
Summer Morning, A, 136
Sunrise Call, The, 138
Sunset Song, 139
Sweet Betsy from Pike, 91
Sweetheart Out a-Hunting, 34
Sweetly Sings the Donkey, 174
Swing on the Corner, 33
Swinging, 18
Swiss Walking Song, 20
There Grew a Rosy Maid, 44
There's a Little Wheel a-Turnin' in My Heart, 85
Three Dukes, 36
Tired Tim, 28
Tootin' Turk, The, 190
Trip to Town, A, 94
Trout Brook in Spring, 161
Tuku, Tuku, Tuu, I'm Calling, 168
Twelve Days of Christmas, 123
Wabash Cannonball, The, 180
Wait for the Wagon, 22
We're All Together Again, 16
When the Chestnut Leaves Were Falling, 151
When Moses Smote the Water, 83
White Dove, 164
White Llamas, 169
Who Has Seen the Wind? 146
Winkum, Winkum, 76
Wondrous Child, The, 120
Work on the Railroad, 53
Young Woman with a Cane, 27

PRINTED IN THE UNITED STATES OF AMERICA